95p

USER MODELLING
IN TEXT
GENERATION

COMMUNICATION IN ARTIFICIAL INTELLIGENCE SERIES

Artificial Intelligence (AI) is a central aspect of Fifth Generation computing, and it is now increasingly recognized that a particularly important element of AI is communication. This series addresses current issues, emphasizing generation as well as comprehension in the AI communication. It covers communication of three types: at the human–computer interface; in computer–computer communication that simulates human interaction; and in the use of computers for machine translation to assist human–human communication. The series also gives a place to research that extends beyond language to consider other systems of communication that humans employ such as pointing, and even in due course, facial expression, body posture, etc.

Communication in Artificial Intelligence Series Editors:
Robin P. Fawcett, Computational Linguistics Unit, University of Wales College of Cardiff
Erich H. Steiner, IAI EUROTRA-D and University of the Saarland

From Syntax to Semantics: Insights from Machine Translation, eds: Erich Steiner, Paul Schmidt and Cornelia Zelinsky-Wibbelt

Advances in Natural Language Generation: An Interdisciplinary Perspective, 2 vols, eds: Michael Zock and Gerard Sabah

Text Generation and Systemic-Functional Linguistics: Experiences from English and Japanese, Christian M.I.M. Matthiessen and John A. Bateman

Expressibility and the Problem of Efficient Text Planning, Marie W. Meteer

Linguistic Issues in Machine Translation, ed.: Frank Van Eynde

New Concepts in Natural Language Generation: Planning, Realization and Systems, eds: Helmut Horacek and Michael Zock

User Modelling in Text Generation, Cecile L. Paris

Text Knowledge and Object Knowledge, Annely Rothkegel

USER MODELLING IN TEXT GENERATION

Cécile L. Paris

Pinter Publishers, London and New York
*distributed in the United States and Canada
by St. Martin's Press, New York*

Pinter Publishers
25 Floral Street, Covent Garden, London, WC2E 9DS, United Kingdom

First published in 1993

© Cécile L. Paris, 1993

Distributed Exclusively in the USA and Canada by St. Martin's Press, Inc., Room 400, 175 Fifth Avenue, New York, NY10010, USA

British Library Cataloguing in Publication Data
A CIP catalogue record for this book is available from the British Library

ISBN 0 86187 809 4

Library of Congress Cataloging-in-Publication Data
A CIP catalog record for this book is available from the Library of Congress

Printed and bound in Great Britain by Biddles Ltd, Guildford and Kings Lynn

To my parents

Contents

List of Figures

Foreword

Those who study language and communication document an explicit relation between speaker and hearer, between writer and reader. Certainly those who communicate effectively plan what they will say based in part on their knowledge of the listener. Computer systems that produce language must also take into account their listeners or readers, in this case the users of the system, in order to be effective. In this book, based on her dissertation, Paris describes an approach that allows a system to tailor the content of a text to a user's level of expertise. Unlike previous approaches that had assumed simply that an expert in the domain of communication needs less information and a novice needs more, Paris found that experts and novices need different kinds of information. This hypothesis is supported by careful study of a variety of texts aimed at different types of audiences. I leave it to Paris to describe the texts studied and the details of the results, but simply note with pleasure that it is solid empirical work.

In the implementation of the generation system, TAILOR, Paris treads middle ground between the rigid use of stereotypes and the use of complex reasoning about speaker and hearer beliefs. The result is a flexible, but practical system that is able to vary the content of text for a wide variety of users spanning a continuum from novice to expert. The variety of possible text that the system can produce is impressive.

As her thesis advisor, I take special pleasure in seeing this work come to print. I hope all readers out there will enjoy it as much as I have enjoyed working with Cécile.

Dr. Kathleen McKeown
Columbia University

Preface

As computer systems become more and more complex, they will need to ensure that they can adapt their behavior to the users with whom they interact. It is extremely unlikely that the same response will be satisfactory for all users, especially as the systems need to interact with an increasingly varied user community in an ever more extensive range of situations.

One of the issues that interactive systems will need to address is that of content selection and organization in responding to user requests. Typically, these systems will have access to very large amounts of data, not all of which can be presented to the user. No single generated text can be adequate across all user types and all situations. Therefore, to be useful, a system must be able to tailor its texts to each user. One aspect of this tailoring (which has been somewhat neglected in the past) is adapting to the user's level of knowledge. This is crucial if the system is to respond to the user in a manner that is both informative and understandable. For example, the system should not present information already known or obvious to the user, and it should not include facts the user cannot understand.

This book describes a text generation system that demonstrates the feasibility of incorporating the user's domain knowledge (or the user's level of expertise) into the generation process. A commonly held previous belief was that the user's level of knowledge only affected the *level of detail* to include in a response. However, our text analyses have shown that this is a simplification of the phenomenon: in reality, the user's domain knowledge affects not only the level of detail, but also *the type of information* that needs to be presented. Furthermore, while most previous systems could only deal with a fixed set of stereotypes, this book presents a method by which a system can tailor its answers to any user, whose level of expertise lies anywhere along the knowledge spectrum, from naive to expert. We describe an implemented text generation system TAILOR, capable of producing multi-sentential descriptions of complex devices (such as telephones and radios) tailored to the user's level of expertise.

The work described in this book was performed at Columbia University. I am grateful to many people who helped in shaping it. First and foremost, I would like to thank my advisors, Michael Lebowitz and Kathleen McKeown, who have provided much help, guidance, and encouragement during my stay at Columbia University. Discussions with them were a fruitful source of ideas and inspiration, and their tireless reading (and re-reading) of my thesis and other work has considerably improved my writing style. John Kender, Jim Corter and David Krantz have been very helpful members of my thesis committee. Steve Feiner and Robin Cohen also made useful comments on this work. Their comments and insights are greatly appreciated. I am thankful to TjoeLiong Kwee for his help in developing the Functional Unification Grammar that TAILOR uses, and to David Benjamin for helping me with LATEXin writing this manuscript.

Discussions of my work with friends and colleagues at Columbia have always been stimulating and enjoyable. Special thanks to Ursula Wolz, Kenny Wasserman, Michelle Baker, Larry Hirsch and the other members of the RESEARCHER project. I also very much appreciated the support and encouragement of Dayton Clark, Don Ferguson, Jim Kurose, Betty Kapetanakis, Channing Brown, Kevin Matthews, Dannie Durand, Moti Yung, Stuart Haber, Galina and Mark Moerdler, and Michael van Biema. Sincere thanks to them all. Yoram Eisenstadter deserves special thanks for his constant encouragement, support and advice.

I would like to express my appreciation to Erich Steiner and Robin Fawcett as well as the Pinter staff for their patience and support in the completion of this manuscript.

At the Information Sciences Institute, where I am now, I subjected yet more people to the reading of this manuscript. In particular, I would like to express my gratitude to John Bateman and Elisabeth Maier for their thorough reading. Johanna Moore deserves special credit for being both a great colleague and a wonderful friend. We have worked together while she was at ISI, and the last chapter of this book presents some of our work. Similarly, my work with John Bateman (also presented in the last chapter of this book) has been (and continues to be!) very enjoyable. I also want to thank Vibhu Mittal and Yolanda Gil for their invaluable help and support when finishing this document.

I am also deeply indebted to Clark Thompson and Joseph Traub without whom I might not have gone to graduate school at all! Finally, and most importantly, many thanks to my family, which has been great in encouraging my work, especially my parents, my brother Guillaume, and our 'little friends'.

Support for the work presented in this book was provided in part by the Defense Advanced Research Projects Agency under contract N00039-84-C-0165, and by the National Science Foundation grant IRI-84-51438. The work presented in the last chapter of this book is supported in part by the Defense Advanced Research Projects Agency (DARPA) under a NASA Ames cooperative agreement number NCC 2-520, and by the National Science Foundation grant IRI-9003087. I also gratefully acknowledge the support of DARPA under the contract DABT63-91-C-0025 while finishing this manuscript.

Chapter 1

Introduction

Sophisticated computer systems capable of interacting with people using natural language are now becoming widespread. These systems need to interact with an increasingly varied user community across an ever more extensive range of situations. Typically, these systems have access to a large amount of data and must select from this data the information to present to the user. No single generated text will be adequate across all user types and all situations. A system will thus be most useful if it can tailor its texts to each user. In particular, a user's level of knowledge about the domain of discourse is an important factor in this tailoring, if the text provided is to be both informative and understandable to the user. The text should not contain information already known or easily inferred by the user, and it should not include facts the user cannot understand. In this book, we demonstrate the feasibility of incorporating the user's domain knowledge, or *user's expertise*, into a text generation system and address the issue of how this factor might affect a text. The results are embodied in TAILOR, a computer system that takes into account this knowledge level to provide object descriptions that are appropriate for users falling anywhere along the knowledge spectrum, from naive to expert.

1.1   Natural Language Generation

One of the aims of Natural Language Processing is to facilitate the use of computers by allowing users to communicate with the computer in natural language. There are two important aspects to human/machine communication: presenting information to the

1

user and understanding a query from the user. The former is the concern of generation.[1] It is recognized that generating a text is a complex problem. In order to be effective, a text must be:

- informative: it must contain information the user does not already know;

- coherent: it must be organized in some coherent manner;

- understandable: it must be stated in terms the user understands and contain information that the user will be able to grasp;

- relevant: it must provide information that will help users achieve their goals;

- appropriate: it must be phrased in an appropriate style and with the correct interpersonal force: depending on the situation, different styles of phrasing are appropriate.

In most cases, generation systems need to determine *what to include* in an answer, *how to organize* the information into a coherent text,[2] and *how to express* the information in language. In a domain containing a great deal of information, deciding what to include in a text is an especially important task as a system cannot simply state all the facts contained in the knowledge base about an entity or an event, but rather must select the most appropriate ones. Organizing the selected facts is also a problem, since they cannot all be output at the same time. The problem of text organization has also been referred to as "linearization," for it involves placing the selected facts into a sequence, e.g., (McDonald, 1980; Brown and Yule, 1983).

One way to organize facts in a coherent manner is to employ a *discourse strategy*. A discourse strategy is knowledge about constructing a coherent text for a given discourse (or communicative) goal. Discourse strategies can in fact be employed to guide a system in deciding both what to include and how to organize it. The tasks of choosing some information to present to the user and organizing it into a coherent text cannot really be divided (Appelt, 1985; Moore and Paris, 1992b). They are intertwined and influence one another in many ways. For example, the information to be included when describing an object by presenting its components (which is one discourse strategy available to describe objects) is different from the information to be included when explaining how the object works (another available strategy). At the same time, the choice of a strategy depends on what knowledge is available. For

---

[1] We are concerned here with presenting information to the user in natural language. Another important issue in this process of communication is that of choosing the appropriate media (e.g., text, graphics. tables, etc). We will not be addressing this issue here. See, e.g., (Mackinlay, 1986; Feiner, 1988; Wahlster *et al.*, 1990; Arens and Hovy, 1990; Binot *et al.*, 1990; Feiner and McKeown, 1990; Neal and Shapiro, 1991; Roth *et al.*, 1991; Feiner and McKeown, 1991; Feiner *et al.*, 1991; Wahlster *et al.*, 1991; McKeown *et al.*, 1992). It is important to note, however, that aspects of the user will also be important in multi-media presentation, e.g., (Elhadad *et al.*, 1991).

[2] Some generation systems, especially early systems, are given as input a set of elements to express and only have the task of organizing them coherently, e.g., (Goldman, 1974; Goldman, 1975; Davey, 1978; Kukich, 1985; Hovy, 1988b). This is not generally the case, however.

example, if the system has no information about the parts of an object, describing it by presenting its parts is no longer possible. Similarly, providing an analogy is only possible in the knowledge base contains analogous concepts.

Often, the generation process is divided into two parts: deciding on the content and organization of a text, selecting the appropriate facts to present to the user and organizing them into a coherent structure; and choosing lexical items and syntactic structures that best express the different facts, in order to produce natural language. This characterization has been used by many researchers to allow them to better study one aspect of the process. Like them, we will use this characterization in this work, as our emphasis is on determining how the user's level of expertise affects the *content* and *organization* of a text. It is important, however, to understand that this is a simplification of the generation process. In reality, just as there are interactions between the tasks of determining the content of a text and the task of organizing it, there must also be interactions between the tasks of determining the content and organization of a text and that of choosing lexical and syntactic structures to express it, to ensure its expressibility. Recently, researchers have started addressing this issue – e.g., (Appelt, 1985; Danlos, 1987; Paris, 1988; Nirenburg *et al.*, 1989; Meteer, 1990; Rubinoff, 1992).

1.1.1   Language variation according to the situation

People speak differently according to the situation. For example, a surgeon will describe some aspects of a surgical operation differently depending on whether he or she is in a briefing room, actually carrying out the operation and talking with other doctors and nurses, or discussing it afterwards with his or her friends; two doctors reviewing a patient's problem will employ precise and 'technical' medical terms; on the other hand, when talking to the patient, they will use a different style of language in order for the patient to understand them. This is illustrated quite strikingly in Figure 1.1.

Similarly, Figure 1.2 presents two descriptions of the same medical term, one to a medical expert such as a physician and the other to a layman such as a patient. It is fairly safe to assume that the patient would not understand 'an unpaired compound gland' or 'cordlike extension of the infundibulum'. A system talking to him or her would therefore have to use more common terms and phrases, such as 'pituitary gland', as well avoid giving various technical details that will most probably not be understood, because the user will not have background knowledge necessary to understand them. However, although the expert may well understand the more naive text, it will in many cases be too general or vague to convey accurate information (since one of the principal characteristics of technical language is its detailed accuracy). So a system that addresses an expert must present the appropriate information in suitably accurate terms.

More generally, language varies depending on its situation of use: instructional texts are linguistically different from reference manuals, news articles are different from editorials and commentaries, and texts for novices are different from text aimed at experts, etc. This linguistic variation is called *functional* or *register* variation. Importantly, this variation permeates all levels of linguistic realization, from the content

When I was training to become an emergency medical technician, the physician in charge stressed the importance of using proper medical terminology. Soon after my graduation, I had to transport a boy with a head wound to the hospital, so I radioed in the description: "Ten-year-old male with ten-centimeter laceration on the left occipital region."

The doctor who had instructed me met us in the emergency room. "What happened, son?" he asked the child. "Did you bop your gourd?"

From (Reader's Digest, 1989).

Figure 1.1: Employing different terms in talking to different people.

medical dictionary (Stedman, 1982):

hypophysis: Glandula pituitaria or basilaris; pituitary or master gland; h. cerebri; an unpaired compound gland suspended from the base of the hypothalamus by a short cordlike extension of the infundibilum, the hypophysial (or pituitary) stalk.

ordinary dictionary (Webster, 1979):

hypophysis: the pituitary gland.

Figure 1.2: Dictionary entries for doctors and non-doctors

and organization of the text as a whole (as in Figure 1.2), to lexical and syntactic constructions of individual sentences (i.e., the phrasing of the text) (as in Figure 1.1).

For text generation systems to be effective, then, they need to provide text appropriate to the situation at hand. If a generation system is to be used only in one single situation (i.e., for one *register*), it only needs to be able to generate text appropriate in that situation. If, on the other hand, it needs to generate texts in several situations, the system must be able to *dynamically* tailor its text to the given situation. The realization that situations *systematically* affect language can greatly help the tailoring process (Bateman and Paris, 1989; Bateman and Paris, 1991). Not only do people talk differently in different situations, but they do so predictably. Specific types of situations have definable properties, which in turn have determinate consequences on language. That is: given appropriate classifications of situation types, the consequences of these situations on language can be specified, and suitable language can be produced. We thus need to study what aspects of situation affect language in a systematic way, and how they affect it.

Register theory within Systemic-Functional Linguistics (Halliday, 1973) has been concerned precisely with the interrelationships between linguistic variation and types of audience and situations, and there has been a large body of work attempting to specify which aspects of situations affect language systematically and how they affect it, e.g., (Cloran, 1987; Gregory, 1967; Hasan, 1978; Hasan, 1984; Hasan, 1989; Mackay and Mountford, 1978; Martin and Rothery, 1981; Ure, 1969; Ure and Ellis,

4

1969; White, 1974; Biber, 1988; Biber, 1989). This theory thus provides a theoretical framework in which one can study the variation of language depending on the situation and the audience. According to this theory, situations can be decomposed into three main components, all of which affect language: the subject matter at hand (e.g., weather reports *vs* a medical domain), the type of communication (e.g., spoken *vs* written, reference texts *vs* tutorials), and the social relationships of the participants (e.g., in terms of their respective levels of expertise). Following Functional Systemic Linguistics, we call these three components *field, mode*, and *tenor* respectively. Register variation thus has three dimensions.

Generation systems typically generate text in restricted register dimensions or address the issue of how language varies depending on *one* dimension of register variation, thus providing the development of part of an overall theory of language generation, constrained with respect to a concrete computational task and implementation. As pointed out in (Matthiessen and Bateman, 1991), the design of text generation systems reflects the purposes for which texts are to be generated. The architecture of TAILOR indeed reflects the fact that it was designed to generate multi-sentential texts appropriate for the user's level of expertise. In TAILOR, we studied one aspect of *tenor register variation*: the user's level of knowledge about the domain. In doing so, we were mainly concerned with the influence of this specific situational characteristic on a specific portion of the generation process: determining the content and organization of a response. The other aspects of register variation were kept constant: TAILOR generates descriptions of complex physical objects such as telephones and radios in a non-interactive fashion. As we will see in Chapter 4, TAILOR uses two discourse strategies to guide its generation process. By studying texts, we were able to identify how the user's level of expertise affected the discourse strategy to be employed. The choice of discourse strategy in turn affects both the content and the organization of the text to be produced. We were thus able to identify how the level of expertise systematically affects the text at the content and organization level.

1.2 User modelling in generation

The fact that a text appropriate for one user may not be adequate for another, and that people make use of their knowledge about other participants in a conversation in order to communicate effectively has also been recognized by researchers in computational linguistics, giving rise to the field called *user modelling*.

Users who are allowed to pose questions to a system in natural language will tend to attribute human-like features to the system, expecting it to respond in the same way a person would (Hayes and Reddy, 1979). Furthermore, natural communication is most often taken as a good model for human/machine communication, e.g., (Winograd and Flores, 1986; Falzon, 1990). If not too costly, then, it would clearly be desirable for a computer system to have knowledge about the user to approximate more closely human communication behavior. This knowledge, contained in what is termed a *user model*, would aid a system in making various decisions required in the course of generating an answer.

User modelling in generation has two aspects: one corresponds to what was referred to above as tenor variation, that is generating language that is linguistically appropriate for a specific user or a class of users. The other aspect corresponds to making use of some characteristic of the user (typically his or her goals and plans) not to vary the *linguistic* aspect of the text but still to *better choose the text's content*.

A user model can contain a variety of facts about a user, including the user's domain knowledge, the user's goal in asking a question, and various attributes about the user that might help a system in both its problem solving activity and its generation process. In this work, we are mainly concerned with studying how the user's *domain knowledge* can affect a text. We will not, however, address the issue of correcting misconceptions, as it has already been addressed at length by other researchers in both generation, e.g., (Mays, 1980a; Joshi *et al.*, 1984; McCoy, 1988; Quilici *et al.*, 1988; McCoy, 1989), and Intelligent Tutoring Systems, e.g., (Brown and Burton, 1978; Stevens *et al.*, 1979; Sleeman and Brown, 1981; Sleeman, 1983; Wenger, 1987).

The tailoring of answers according to domain knowledge is used extensively by humans. An explanation of how a car engine works aimed at a child will be different than one aimed at an adult, and an explanation adequate for a music student is probably too superficial for a student of mechanical engineering. There is further evidence of this phenomenon in naturally occurring texts, where the type of information presented to readers varies with their probable level of domain knowledge. (We present such evidence in Chapter 3.) A text generation system thus needs to take into consideration the user's domain knowledge level to construct an appropriate text.

The need for a model of the user's domain knowledge in question answering systems has been noted by various researchers, e.g., (Lehnert, 1977; Lehnert, 1978; McKeown, 1985). The programs that have modelled the user's domain knowledge, however, did so only in order to generate more or less detailed texts, assuming the *level of detail* was the only parameter to vary, e.g., (Wallis and Shortliffe, 1982; Sleeman, 1985). They did not address the issue of whether or not this assumption was valid. We do address this problem here, identifying the role played by the user's level of knowledge in determining the contentcontent and organization of a text. Our primary domain in investigating this problem concerns the description of complex devices, such as telephones, and radios.

1.3   Research method and major results

Our goal was thus to determine whether the readers' assumed knowledge was an important factor in the communication process, and therefore worth modelling in a computer system, and to identify how this factor affected the generation process. Natural language generation provides us with a good test-bed for user modelling issues: we can study texts (or dialogues) produced by humans, analyze their differences and postulate which aspects of the user can account for these differences. By then implementing the resulting theory in a generation system and varying the user model given to the system, we can evaluate the texts produced (by comparing them to the original texts, for example) to test the theory. This methodology, commonly employed in generation and user modelling, is the methodology we employed in this work.

To determine how people describe complex devices and see whether these descriptions differ with the readers' assumed level of knowledge about the domain, we analyzed various naturally occurring texts. We looked at texts aimed at readers on the two ends of the knowledge spectrum: naive and expert. The text analyses indicated that the user's level of expertise affects the *kind* of information and not just the *amount of detail* presented. This result is significant as it demonstrates that level of detail is not the *only* factor to consider in tailoring a text to a user's level of knowledge.

We characterized these results in terms of two discourse strategies used to present texts to readers with different knowledge levels. One of these strategies, the *constituency schema*, is composed of linguistically defined predicates and was identified in previous work on generation by McKeown (1985). As will be explained in Chapter 3, this strategy is a *declarative* strategy, i.e., it is based on an abstract characterization of patterns occurring in many texts and is independent of the structure of the underlying knowledge base. Rather, it *imposes* a structure on the underlying knowledge base. The other strategy, the *process trace*, is a new type of strategy that we term a *procedural* strategy. This strategy consists of *directives*, or directions on how to trace the knowledge base. The structure of a text generated using this strategy mirrors the structure of the underlying knowledge base in ways dictated by the strategy. In contrast, texts produced by declarative strategies (such as the constituency schema) mirror the abstract patterns represented in the strategies. We have developed a precise formalization of the process trace. These two strategies will be presented in detail in Chapter 4.

We show how these strategies can be combined to provide answers to users whose domain knowledge falls *anywhere along* the knowledge spectrum, from naive to expert. We have implemented these strategies in TAILOR, a program that generates device descriptions appropriate for users with varying expertise.

In summary, this book first illustrates the methodology employed in generation and user modelling to identify factors that are important in the communication process. Then it demonstrates how a generation system can exploit a user model in order to provide answers tailored to the user. In particular, this work shows the feasibility of incorporating the user's *domain knowledge* into a generation system, adding a dimension to the register variation considered by current generation systems. It provides a specification of how the level of expertise of the user affects the generation process, namely it affects the content and the organization of the text to be generated, and not only the amount of detail. Finally, it describes how this register variation (or this tailoring) can be implemented in a text generation system.

Patent: US # 3899794, 12 Aug 1975

Title: Front Loading Disc Drive Apparatus
Inventor: Brown Leon Henry, Sylmar, CA, United States
            Wangco Incorporated (US Corporation)

Apparatus for receiving and driving magnetic disc cartridges as peripheral computer memory units. Particular mechanisms are included which render the apparatus more effective and more compact than previously known corresponding devices of a comparable nature. These mechanisms cooperate to provide means for inserting the disc cartridge in a horizontal attitude, permitting the apparatus to be completely contained within a reduced vertical dimension and thus saving substantial space. These mechanisms are operatively coupled to the loading door so that, as the loading door is rotated through approximately 60 degrees to its open position, a pair of actuators coupled thereto are rotated through approximately 90 degrees to first lift and then translate the disc cartridge receiver forward to its fully extended position. During this motion, various door opener levers which are associated with the receiver for the purpose of opening the head entry door of the disc cartridge to the extent necessary to permit entry of the heads therein when the cartridge and receiver are in the retracted position for operation within the disc drive apparatus are withdrawn so that the head entry door may be closed when the cartridge is withdrawn from the receiver. When the cartridge is inserted within the receiver, the head entry door is opened to a first extent by a pivoted bail member and the reverse of the above-described operations occurs as the loading door is closed so as to retract the receiver with the disc cartridge therein to the operating position.

Figure 1.3: Example of a patent abstract

1.4   The domain

Our domain is that of RESEARCHER, a program developed at Columbia University to read, remember and generalize from patent abstracts (Lebowitz, 1983b; Lebowitz, 1985). The abstracts describe complex devices in which spatial and functional relations are important. An example of a patent abstract is shown in Figure 1.3.

The knowledge base constructed from reading patents is large and detailed. This domain is a challenging one for language generation as there are several different kinds of information and many details from which to select facts to present to the user, rendering the decision process a complicated one. TAILOR, the generation system presented in this book, produces natural language descriptions of devices from RESEARCHER's knowledge base.[3] Figure 1.4 presents a block diagram of how TAILOR and RESEARCHER

---

[3] As the research for building the parser for RESEARCHER was being done at the same time as this research,

8

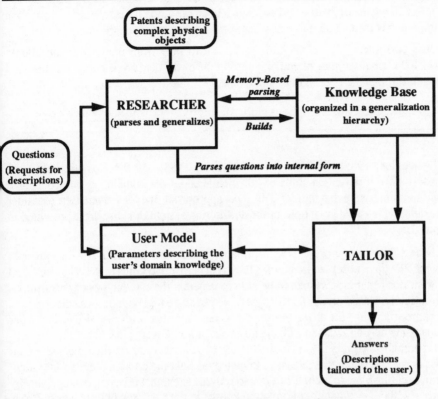

Figure 1.4: RESEARCHER and the TAILOR System

interact. Upon receiving a request for a description, TAILOR uses discourse strategies to guide its decision process and examines both the knowledge base and the user model to determine the content and organization of the text to be generated.

Generating descriptions is a difficult generation task in TAILOR's domain because a request for the description of an object cannot be answered by straightforward retrieval from the knowledge base. There are no clear constraints on what information should be included in the answer. This type of question is termed a *high-level question* (Tennant, 1978; Tennant, 1981; McKeown, 1985).

To produce a description, a program cannot just state all the facts contained in the knowledge base about the object as there will typically be too many. A generation system will require guidance to select the appropriate facts to present to the user. Previous research efforts have developed discourse strategies to guide a system in choosing facts from a knowledge base in order to generate *coherent* texts, e.g., (Davey,

---

the knowledge base was coded by hand in some cases. It is, however, faithful to the representation built by RESEARCHER.

1. It has an enclosure, two breather filters and an air guide for directing air flow. One of the filters is located on the enclosure top while the other is on the enclosure bottom.

2. The two filters and an air guide causes air to flow from the outside, be filtered through the top filter, pass directly on the spindle of the disc drive and on the disc, and pass out through the bottom filter to the outside.

Figure 1.5: Two descriptions of the air filtering mechanism of a disc-drive

1978; Kukich, 1985; Kukich, 1983; McKeown, 1985). In this domain, users will probably have different amounts of knowledge about the domain, so that coherence alone does not ensure that the text is the most appropriate one for a given user. Consider for example the two descriptions of the air filtering system of a disc drive presented in Figure 1.5.

Both these descriptions present the information in a coherent manner. Yet they differ in content. We have observed in our data the existence of two kinds of descriptions,[4] and we want our generation system to be able to generate these two types of descriptions appropriately. Based on our text analyses, we postulate that both of these descriptions are appropriate, but for different users: a person familiar with disc drives and filter mechanisms may be satisfied with the first description. On the other hand, that description is probably not very informative to a user who has never seen a filter mechanism on a disc drive. We argue that the user's knowledge about the domain plays an important role in deciding what to include in a text to provide a text that is best understandable by the user without giving only information known to the user, and that such knowledge can guide a generation system.

1.5 System overview

A block diagram of TAILOR is shown in Figure 1.6. TAILOR receives as input a request for a description and a set of parameters that describe a user's knowledge about the domain. This request is passed to the *textual component*. This component, the main concern in this work, determines the content and organization of the description to be generated. It is guided in its decision process by the user model and the two discourse strategies that were identified from our text analyses. The strategy choice depends on the content of the user model.

The output of the textual component, a description in internal representation, is passed to the *tactical component*. The tactical component consists of a *dictionary interface* and a *surface generator*. The interface chooses the lexical items and syntactic structures. The

---

[4]There are yet more views one can take of an object (Stevens and Steinberg, 1981), some of which are useful in different contexts, such as Intelligent Computer Aided Instruction. We restrict ourselves, however, to the types of descriptions we found in the texts we analyzed, which correspond to descriptions given to users with varying level of knowledge about the domain of interaction.

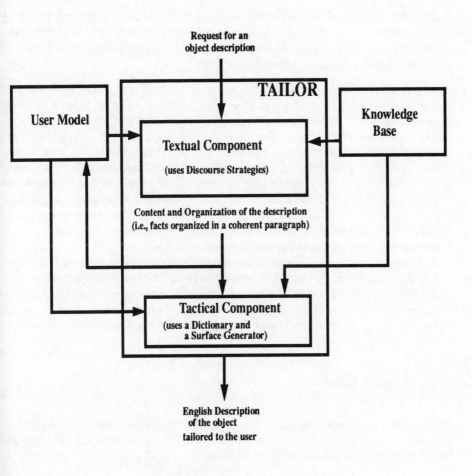

Figure 1.6: The TAILOR System

surface generator produces English sentences using a Functional Unification Grammar (Kay, 1979).

1.6 Examples from TAILOR

Sample texts generated by TAILOR are presented in the Figures 1.7 through 1.11. All texts appearing in this typeface in this book have been generated by TAILOR. Each one is preceded by a description of the user model for which the text was generated and the name of the object being described.

In Figure 1.7, the user is a naive user. As we have found appropriate from our text analyses, the system chooses a discourse strategy that explains to the user how the object performs its function, so that the user can build a functional model of the object. In Figure 1.8, the user is already familiar with two objects in the knowledge base, the loudspeaker and the microphone. Because these two objects essentially form a telephone, the system chooses to describe the telephone by describing mainly its structural aspects, assuming the user will be able to build a functional model of the telephone based on his or her knowledge about the microphone and the loudspeaker. Similarly, in Figure 1.9, as the user is familiar with a closely related object (the loudspeaker), only a structural description of the telephone receiver is given. In Figure 1.10, the user does not know any object in the knowledge base but understands the concepts of electricity and voltages. The system thus provides a functional description of a vacuum-tube, and is able to use concepts and terms related to electricity and voltages as the user is familiar with these. Finally, in Figure 1.11, a description that mixes the two strategies (structural and functional) is given as the user knows about some aspects of the object to be described but not others. More examples will be given throughout the book.

1.7 Limitations

In this work, we do not examine in depth the problem of determining how much the user knows about the domain, but take the user model as given. We will briefly discuss how it might be inferred in Chapter 2.

In order to focus on the role of a user's level of expertise in generation, other problems had to be ignored. We have not considered user characteristics other than domain knowledge, even though this is not the only factor which can influence an answer. In particular, we have not studied the influence of users' goals and plans. Inferring the user's goals and plans is another very hard problem and there has been much research on the subject, e.g., (Allen and Perrault, 1980; Carberry, 1983; McKeown *et al.*, 1985; Pollack, 1986). It would, of course, be interesting to study the interaction of the users' goals and domain knowledge in determining the content of an answer, as started in (Wolz, 1990; Wolz *et al.*, 1990; Sarner and Carberry, 1992).

User Model:
    Objects known – nil

Describe telephone (short description)

TAILOR output:

A telephone is a device that transmits soundwaves. Because a person speaks into the transmitter of a telephone, a varying current is produced. Then, the current flows through the receiver. This causes soundwaves to be reproduced.

Figure 1.7: Short description of a telephone

User Model:
    Objects known – loudspeaker, microphone

Describe telephone

TAILOR output:

A telephone is a device that transmits soundwaves. The telephone has a housing that has various shapes and various colors, a transmitter that changes soundwaves into current, a curly-shaped cord, a line, a receiver to change current into soundwaves and a dialing-mechanism. The transmitter is a microphone with a small disc-shaped metal thin diaphragm. The receiver is a loudspeaker with a small aluminum diaphragm. The housing contains the transmitter, and it contains the receiver. The housing is connected to the dialing-mechanism by the cord. The line connects the dialing-mechanism to the wall.

Figure 1.8: Description of a telephone

User Model:
> *Objects know – ?* loudspeaker

Describe telephone receiver

TAILOR output:

A receiver is a loudspeaker with a small metal disc-shaped diaphragm. A receiver has a permendur ring-shaped armature, a coil, a ring-shaped permanent magnet, a gap and a small metal disc-shaped diaphragm. The diaphragm is mounted on the poles of the magnet. The gap contains air, and it is between the diaphragm and the poles. The coil is mounted around the magnet.

Figure 1.9: Description of a receiver

User Model:
> *Objects known –* nil
> *Concepts known –* electricity, voltage

Describe a vacuum-tube

TAILOR output:

A vacuum-tube is a device that produces a strong current from a power-source across the anode and the cathode. Because a heat source heats the cathode, electrons accumulate on the cathode. The cathode is made of metal. Electrons accumulating on the cathode enables electrons to flow towards the anode. Because the power-source produces voltage across the anode and the cathode, electrons flow towards the anode. This causes strong current across the anode and the cathode to be produced.

Figure 1.10: Description of a vacuum-tube

User Model
> *Objects known* – microphone, loudspeaker
> *Concepts known* – electricity

Describe a pulse telephone

TAILOR output:

A pulse-telephone is a telephone with a pulse dialer. The pulse-telephone has a pulse-dialer that produces current pulses when a person dials, a housing that has various shapes and various colors, a receiver to change a current into soundwaves, a curly-shaped cord, a line and a transmitter that changes soundwaves into a current. The pulse dialer is a dialing mechanism. Because a person dials, the dial assembly of the pulse dialer turns clockwise. This causes the spring of the pulse dialer to be compressed. The spring is circular. The compression of the spring enables the spring to be decompressed. Because the person dials, the person releases the dial of the dial-assembly. This causes the spring to be decompressed. The decompression of the spring causes the dial assembly to turn counterclockwise. This causes the gear of the pulse-dialer to turn. The gear is small. The dial-assembly turns counterclockwise proportionally to the way the gear turns. Because the gear turns, the protrusion of the gear hits the lever of the switch. This causes the lever to close the switch. Because the lever closes the switch, current pulses are produced. The receiver is a loudspeaker with a small metal thin disk-shaped diaphragm. The dialing-mechanism is connected to a wall by the line. The housing is connected to the dialing mechanism by the cord. The housing contains the transmitter, and it contains the receiver. The transmitter is a microphone with a thin disk-shaped small diaphragm.

Figure 1.11: Description of a pulse-telephone

Requests for descriptions are the only type of questions we have studied in TAILOR. We believe that descriptions are a good starting point as they are often required to answer other types of questions, and we feel that a user's domain knowledge will affect other types of questions as well.

Finally, we have made no attempt to parse questions from English input. (We will briefly discuss in Section 2 how a query posed to the system might also suggest the appropriate response level.) Moreover, while TAILOR does generate English sentences, we have studied neither the influence of a user's domain knowledge on lexical choice nor the complexity and subtleties of surface generation. Our emphasis has been on deep generation. In Chapter 8, we will briefly discuss current work that aims at extending this work to address precisely this limitation.

1.8   A guide to remaining chapters

First, in Chapter 2, we describe the *kinds* of knowledge a user possesses about a domain that can affect generation and be explicitly represented in a user model. Instances of these kinds of knowledge will be the information contained in TAILOR's user model. Having identified what needs to be in the user model, we will take the user model as given, and study how a system can use the information contained in the user model to tailor the answer. This chapter also discusses how the user model needed for TAILOR might be obtained. We then present our text analyses in Chapter 3, showing how texts aimed at two distinct audiences (expert and naive) are organized differently and present different types of information to their readers. There, we introduce the two discourse strategies that TAILOR uses to describe complex devices. Each of these strategies is discussed in detail in Chapter 4. TAILOR can combine the two strategies to describe objects to users with intermediate levels of expertise, and, because of the explicit representation employed for the user model, TAILOR can generate descriptions tailored to a whole range of users, without requiring an *a priori* set of user types. This is explained in Chapter 5. TAILOR's implementation is presented in Chapter 6. In Chapter 7, we present an overview of related work in generation and user modelling. Finally, Chapter 8 presents a discussion of the feasibility of this approach, as well as an overview of the research directions that have followed this work.

Chapter 2

The user model in TAILOR

2.1 Contents and use of a user model

A *user model* refers to the knowledge a computer system has about the user. This knowledge affects both a system's behavior and its communication with the user. All systems have a model of the user, which can be implicit in the design of the system, or explicitly represented: all systems are designed with some users in mind, and the type of users envisioned for a specific system usually affects the design of the system and the form of its interaction with its users. More recently, researchers have explored the use of *explicit* user models: that is the knowledge about the user is *explicitly* represented and modifiable, and the system contains mechanisms to exploit this explicit information to adapt its behavior to specific users dynamically.[1] This is the type of user model we are concerned with here.

In general, this user model can contain a variety of information about the user, including:[2]

- *The user's domain knowledge.* This refers to what and how much background knowledge the user already has about the domain under consideration. To

---

[1] Some researchers restrict the definition of *user model* to an explicit model, e.g., (Kobsa and Wahlster, 1989).

[2] See (Kobsa and Wahlster, 1988; Kobsa and Wahlster, 1989; Wahlster and Kobsa, 1989; McTear, 1989; Allen, 1990) and (Chappel and Cahour, 1991) for surveys of different types of user models and of systems that employ user models. See (Cahour and Paris, 1991) for a study identifying more precisely which type of user model is required by which type of system and task.

construct an answer that is not obvious to the user and does not assume knowledge the user does not have, a system needs to know about a user's domain knowledge. Furthermore, the user might have erroneous knowledge about the world, i.e., he or she might have misconceptions about the domain under consideration. In such a case, it is desirable for a system to correct these misconceptions, e.g., (Kaplan, 1982; Mays, 1980a; McCoy, 1986; McCoy, 1988; McCoy, 1989).

- *The user's goals and plans.* The user's goals can modify the meaning of the question, as well as the answer, as an appropriate answer is one that addresses the goal of the user. Furthermore, an answer can also be affected by how the user intended to achieve his or her goals, that is can be affected by the user's plans, e.g., (Hobbs and Robinson, 1978; Allen and Perrault, 1980; Carberry, 1983; van Beek, 1986; Pollack, 1986; Carberry, 1988; McKeown *et al.*, 1985; Carberry, 1990; Wolz, 1990; Wolz *et al.*, 1990; Retz-Schmidt, 1991; Goodman and Litman, 1992; Sarner and Carberry, 1992).

- *Specific beliefs the user has about the domain.* These are the facts that currently happen to be true in the "world." This differs from the user's domain knowledge as it refers to facts known to be true *now* as opposed to facts known to be *always* true in the domain. Mutual beliefs of the speaker and the hearer can be used to plan the production of a referring expression that can be unambiguously understood by the hearer, e.g., (Wahlster *et al.*, 1978; Appelt, 1985; Hoeppner *et al.*, 1984).

- *Specific preferences or interests*: the user might have specific preferences with respect to the domain, and these can affect problem solving: for example, a system making hotel reservations takes into consideration the user's preferences as to the type of room desired (i.e., large, bright, quiet, etc.) (van Hahn *et al.*, 1980; Hoeppner *et al.*, 1984). Preferences can also refer to preferences with respect to presentation modality – i.e., some users might prefer graphic presentations to textual presentations), or to specific rhetorical devices – i.e., some people prefer learning by examples, other by analogies, etc. e.g., (Sarner and Carberry, 1992).

- A *description of the grammatical resources understood or preferred by the user*: especially when dealing with technical domains, the user might not know all the technical terms referring to concepts in the domain. Often, however, these concepts can also be referred to with non-technical words. A user model might indicate the words known (unknown) to the user. It could also indicate the types of syntactic structures that are preferred by the user (or a group of users).

- *Some attributes about the user*: These are attributes of the user other than the ones mentioned above that might help a system in both its problem solving activity and its generation process, e.g., (Rich, 1979; Hovy, 1988a; Chappel and Cahour, 1991). For example, in a system that was acting as a librarian and was selecting books for the user, attributes such as "feminist" or "religious" were used by the system to help selecting books (Rich, 1979).

In general, the information contained in a user model is based on what is observed in natural interactions for similar situations. For example, researchers concerned with diagnosis or consulting systems have studied natural interactions to determine what characteristics of the user experts take into consideration to perform their problem solving activity. Similarly, by studying texts and other type of interactions, researchers identify which aspects of the user affect the presentation. They can then test their hypothesis by implementing them in a system and examining the behavior of the system. In general, the content of a user model will depend on the tasks and goals of a system (Cahour and Paris, 1991).

Researchers have explored various aspects of user modelling: what information is to be represented to enhance a specific task, how to represent this information, how to obtain this information, how to build user modelling shells, and, finally, how to exploit a user model in a system. In TAILOR, we were concerned with identifying how the user's knowledge affects the generation process, as well as with providing mechanisms to allow an generation system to exploit a user model containing the user's level of expertise to enhance the texts to present to the user. As we wanted our system to adapt its behavior to the current user, TAILOR's user model is *explicitly* encoded and *modifiable*. Since this is the focus of this work, the user model contains exclusively information about the user's domain knowledge.

In the remainder of this chapter, we describe the user model employed by TAILOR and explain how the information contained in the user model might be obtained.

2.2 Identifying what needs to be in the user model

As mentioned above, the information to be included in a user model is determined by studying natural interactions (or natural text) and determining which aspects of the user were probably taken into consideration by people in either their problem solving activity or their communications. In this work, we analyzed natural language texts to identify which types of knowledge seemed to affect the production of a text in our domain. Furthermore, although knowledge is multidimensional in the sense that it is possible to be knowledgeable about a domain along several dimensions, such as historical, economical, functional, etc., we restricted ourselves to the types of knowledge that are explicitly represented in terms of our knowledge base.

Analyses of natural language texts suggests the existence of at least two kinds of domain knowledge that affect generation in this domain:

- *knowledge about specific items in the knowledge base.* We define "knowing" about an object to mean knowing about the existence of the object, its purpose and how this purpose is achieved (that is, how the various subparts of the object work together to achieve it). Knowing about an object thus means understanding the functionality of the object and the mechanical processes associated with it.[3]

---

[3]Note that this definition of knowing about a concept differs from Kass (1991, p 230), in which the

---

Telegraph

A telegraph consisted of a key (switch) and an electromagnet (sounder) at each end, in series with a wire and a battery. The earth acted as the return line.

Figure 2.1: Description of a telegraph from *Collier Encyclopedia* (1962)

- *knowledge about various basic underlying concepts*. In a domain of complex physical objects, such concepts might include *electricity* and *voltage*. In fact, knowing about these concepts also implies knowing various other notions associated with these concepts. For example, knowing about *electricity* implies knowing about *current, circuit,* etc. Given a specific domain, one has to identify what these concepts are and specify them to a system.

Consider for example the text in Figure 2.1, taken from *Collier Encyclopedia* (1962). The writer of this text must have assumed that the reader would know what a *switch* is, as well as what it meant to be *in series* and to *act as the return line*, thus understanding the concept of *electricity*. The text would probably have been different had the intended readers not have that knowledge.

We define an *expert* user as one whose knowledge about the domain includes functionality of most objects and mechanical processes. An expert user does not necessarily know about *all* the objects contained in the knowledge base however, and thus might ask questions about objects he or she does not know about. Given an object that is new but similar to a known one, an expert user has enough domain knowledge to infer how the parts of this new object work together to perform a function. For example, an expert user might already know about particular instances of this object, or, on the other hand, about generalizations of the object. A *naive* user is one who does not know about specific objects in the knowledge base and does not understand the underlying basic concepts.

A user is not necessarily naive or expert, however. For example, users may know about several objects in the knowledge base. Such users would not be considered naive, but, as there are many objects they do not know in the domain, they would not be considered experts either.

The level of expertise can be seen as a continuum from naive to expert. To really know and understand some of the objects in the knowledge base, a user first needs to understand the basic underlying concepts. When users have mastered these concepts, they become progressively more expert as they acquire knowledge about more objects

---

assertion (BEL HEARER C) is intended to mean that the user knows only the *existence* of the concept C and does not imply that the user knows a definition, any properties of the concept, or any information about it. Our use of this assertion in the user model is closer to (Moore and Paris, 1992a).

in the knowledge base. Most users would fall *between* the extremes of naive and expert. Any user might lack knowledge about specific parts in the domain but understand various basic concepts. For example, a user may not know anything about telephones or similar devices, but still have knowledge about electricity and voltage. Although some combination of the two types of knowledge might not be realistic, the generation program that takes the user's domain knowledge into consideration ought to be able to handle any user model.

We do not attempt in this work either to determine how many stereotypes exist between the two extremes, nor to categorize a user into one of these user types. While defining stereotypes such as *novice, beginner, intermediate* and *advanced* is useful in some domains, such as the UNIX system, for example, where it is possible to associate a set of commands users of a particular stereotype are likely to know (Chin, 1986; 1987; 1988), it is not as applicable in the domain of complex devices, where it is hard to partition the knowledge base into a few categories and decide that knowing about one type of objects implies more expertise than knowing about another set of objects. For example, there is no reason to believe that knowing about microphones indicates more expertise about the domain of complex devices than knowing about telescopes. Instead, we use *explicit* parameters to indicate the user's knowledge. These parameters correspond to the two kinds of knowledge outlined above. They are:

- a list of items in the knowledge base which are known to the user, representing the user's *local expertise*. As an example, a user model in TAILOR may indicate that the user only has *local expertise* with respect to disk drives.

- a list of underlying basic concepts that the user understands. For example, a user model may indicate that the user understands the concept of electricity.

The terminology *naive* and *expert* is retained only for users at the two ends of the knowledge spectrum, *only* as a short-hand notation. The emphasis of this work is on studying how object descriptions can be varied when the content of the user model varies.

By explicitly representing elements of a user's knowledge, we gain the flexibility needed to tailor descriptions to specific users falling anywhere along the knowledge spectrum, without requiring a predefined set of stereotypes. This will be explained in detail in Chapter 5.

2.3   Determining the level of expertise

Although the issue of determining the level of expertise of the user is not addressed in this work, it is obviously an important question that needs to be studied. Much work has already been done in this area, e.g., (Rich, 1979; Kobsa, 1984; Sleeman, 1985; Chin, 1989; Mastaglio, 1990; Bunt, 1990; Kass, 1991b; Shifroni and Shanon, 1992; Wu, 1991; Ballim and Wilks, 1991). In this section, we discuss how the user model for TAILOR might be obtained. Because it is a coarse grained model, we believe that it may be possible to infer it from various factors, as outlined below.

2.3.1   User type

Before the program has been able to gather specific information about a user, *user types* might provide a good *initial heuristic* as a starting point for building a more adequate user model, as classes of users may be likely to be naive while others may be likely to be expert. This method has been used successfully in other systems, such as, for example, the GRUNDY system (Rich, 1979), KNOME (Chin, 1989), or in the explanation module of the EES system, in which the user model is built from a canonical user model, stereotypes, and specific information (Moore and Paris, 1992a). This is also the approach proposed by Cohen and Jones (1989) for building a user model in an educational diagnosis expert system, where psychologists might know one aspect of the knowledge base, while teachers might know another.

For example, three plausible categories of potential users have been identified for RESEARCHER:

- Inventors who created a device and want to check what has already been patented in the domain of their inventions. Inventors are experts in their field, but may be novices in other fields and as far as doing a patent search is concerned.

- Lawyers who perform patent searches for their clients. Unlike the inventors, they are experts with respect to doing a patent search, but are likely to be novices with respect to the contents of the patents.

- General users who are people who want to know what kind of information is available from the database. Such a person could be either an expert or a novice.

Other user types might also be helpful to give *a priori* information on the probable level of expertise, as a class of users may be likely to know about some subset of objects. For example, students in astronomy are likely to know about telescopes, but they won't necessarily have any knowledge about any other objects in the knowledge base. On the other hand, an electrical engineering student is likely to understand concepts such as electricity and know about objects such as microphones. Identifying a user as part of these classes can give insight into how much that user might know, and thus provide a starting point for building the user model.

2.3.2   Obtaining information from a dialogue

Vocabulary and terms employed

The terms employed by the user to ask a question as well as the question type can give some useful information as to how much the user knows about the domain.

Specific vocabulary employed (i.e., technical or not, characteristic of a certain class of users, etc.) can provide information about the user's level of expertise, and can be used, for example, to trigger a stereotype, e.g., (Chin, 1989; Chappel and Cahour, 1991). Yet more information can be obtained from a user's utterance: Intuitively, a person who talks only in very general terms about an object probably does not know much about it. In contrast, knowledge about an *obscure* part of an object usually indicates that a person has some expertise about the domain. The specificity of a question can thus provide information about the user's domain knowledge. As an example, consider the questions Q1 and Q2.

Q1: How is the IBM 3380 disk drive different from the IBM 3330 disk drive?

Q2: How are the three spaced bearings of a disk drive head assembly connected to the tracks ?

If a user knows about the IBM 3380 disk drive, it is likely that he or she has some knowledge about disk drives in general. Likewise, it is certainly not obvious to everyone that a head assembly should include "three spaced bearings", and therefore we might assume that the user has some knowledge about head assemblies. The bearings constitute *obscure* parts of a head assembly, and the fact that the user knows about them indicates a certain level of expertise in the domain.

Memory organization can play a role in determining that a part is obscure. Memory in RESEARCHER, for example, is organized in terms of generalizations (Lebowitz, 1983b; Lebowitz, 1983a). As it reads patents abstracts, RESEARCHER looks for similarities among the objects described to make generalizations from them, and organize its memory around those generalizations. The resulting memory is largely hierarchical, consisting basically of several generalization trees with individual instances at the leaves. The top node in the generalization tree contains information common to all instances of that generalization, while instance nodes only contain information special to that instance.

This complex, hierarchical structure can help determine which parts are obscure. When a user is knowledgeable about a part occurring deep in the generalization tree (the extreme case being a part which is particular only to an instance at the bottom of the tree), we might assume expertise in that subdomain.[4] On the other hand, if only parts at a top level node of the generalization tree are mentioned (i.e., the user knows only about information common to a whole class of objects), then we are probably dealing with a novice in that particular subdomain. Similarly, the depth in the components tree of the knowledge base can help evaluate the user's level of expertise, where a part occurring deep in the parts tree might be more obscure than a part occurring at a higher level. This technique can be helpful in determining the level of expertise of the user in any application using a hierarchical knowledge base.

---

[4] This assumes that the knowledge base is fairly complete, in that it contains more than one object in the generalization tree.

Question type

The type of question asked can also give information about how much the user knows. Consider for example the two questions:

Q1: How many bearings are there?

Q2: What is a bearing?

In Q1, the user most probably knows what a bearing is. In Q2, however, it is clear that this is not the case. The distinction must therefore be made between *knowing* and *mentioning* an object, and we must be careful in applying a method like the one outlined above for determining whether an object is obscure or not. The question type must be used in conjunction with the depth in the knowledge base.

Furthermore, a term may be misused as in "Which filters have flying heads?," when the knowledge base indicates that a "filter" cannot have a "flying head." In this case, the user has a misconception. Techniques like those developed by Kaplan (1982) and Mays (1980b) can be applied to detect the misconceptions. The misconception, in fact, can also be used to infer information about the user's level of expertise.

2.3.3   Employing Inference Rules

Expertise in a subpart of a domain does not necessarily imply expertise in the whole domain. As an example, a user could be an expert in the domain of disk drives without knowing much about the computers that use them (or vice versa: a user could know about computers without really knowing much about disc drives). On the other hand, expertise about microphones might imply expertise about loudspeakers, as their mechanisms are similar. Knowing that the user is familiar with some items of the knowledge base might allow a system to infer expertise about other items. It is thus possible to have some inference rules that would allow a system to define an area of expertise for a given user, or a *radius of expertise*. These inference rules would relate items and concepts, as in (Sleeman, 1985). A system could also have more general rules. For example, when a user mentions a part deep in the generalization tree, expertise with respect to a number of objects related to that part can be established. Or when an item is known to the user, it might be possible to infer that its superordinate in the generalization hierarchy is also known to the user. Similarly, it might be possible to infer knowledge about certain basic concepts, knowing the user has local expertise about some particular entities. In recent work, researchers concerned with building user models have in fact defined sets of inference rules of this kind , e.g., (Bunt, 1990; Kass, 1991a). TAILOR uses two general inference rules of this kind: given local expertise about an object, TAILOR assumes that the user also knows about the superordinate of the object; and, given local expertise about an object, TAILOR assumes that the user also knows about the subparts of the object.

2.3.4   Asking the user questions and using the previous discourse

It is possible to ask the user a few questions about himself to get a starting point for the user model. This is the approach take in both GRUNDY (Rich, 1979) and UMFE (Sleeman, 1985) for example. After the discourse has begun, it may also be advantageous to use the past discourse to update the user model. In TAILOR, for example, once the system has provided a description to a user, it adds the object just described to the user model, assuming the user now knows about the object. While this approach is naive (as it assumes a perfect learner), it allows for the user model to get built up as the discourse progresses. It is possible to relax the assumption of a perfect learner. For example, if a user asks the same question twice, it is indicative that the answer was not understood, perhaps because it assumed knowledge the user did not have (Moore and Paris, 1992a). The user model can be updated correctly to reflect this fact.

2.4   Conclusions

In this chapter, TAILOR's user model has been presented, together with suggestions on how this model might be obtained from various sources. It would, of course, be necessary to study in depth how the user's domain knowledge can be inferred from the sources outlined above and how these sources can be used together. While this is a hard problem, aspects of it have already been addressed in previous research e.g.,(Rich, 1979; Kobsa, 1984; Sleeman, 1985; Chin, 1989; Mastaglio, 1990; Bunt, 1990; Kass, 1991b; Shifroni and Shanon, 1992; Ballim and Wilks, 1991; Wu, 1991), and we believe that it is possible for a system to obtain the user model required by TAILOR.

Chapter 3

The text analysis

This chapter presents the research approach we employed to determine whether descriptions of complex devices varied depending on the assumed level of expertise of the intended readers. As others – e.g., Hasan (1978, 1979), van Dijk (1980), Ventola (1983, 1984), McKeown (1985), Mann and Thompson (1987, 1988), we take the view that people use standard patterns of discourse to achieve a given communicative (or discourse) goal in a given situation, and that these standard patterns can be characterized in terms of discourse strategies. To produce multi-sentential texts, text generation systems can then employ these strategies to guide them in deciding what to say and how to organize it, – e.g., (Weiner, 1980; McKeown, 1985; Kukich, 1985; McCoy, 1986; Moore and Paris, 1992b). Our aim therefore was to identify the different strategies used in human-authored texts to describe devices to audience with different levels of expertise.

In general, discourse strategies are studied by analyzing texts written by people or conversations among two (or several) agents. We chose the former, because of the availability of texts describing objects. To see how the strategies vary depending on a reader's assumed level of expertise, we looked at a variety of texts, including encyclopedia entries, from both adult and junior encyclopedias, high school text books and manuals. This chapter presents the methods employed for the text analysis, examples of the texts studied, the analysis of their organizational structure, and, finally, the two distinct discourse strategies found to describe complex devices.

3.1   Analyzing text

Researchers have identified discourse strategies by decomposing naturally occurring texts with a common discourse goal into rhetorical structures, and identifying patterns that occur across the texts. For example, McKeown (1985) analyzed a variety of texts and found that certain combinations of *rhetorical predicates* were associated with discourse purposes such as providing definitions, comparisons, and descriptions. Mann and Thompson (1987, 1988) identified about 25 *rhetorical relations* found in a diverse collection of texts, ranging from administrative memos to newspaper articles. Furthermore, they also identified some schemata, that is typical combinations of rhetorical relations. Similarly, McCoy (1986) identified combinations of rhetorical predicates that are appropriate for correcting different types of user misconceptions. These patterns, which may contain options, are then captured formally in discourse strategies for the discourse goal of the texts studied.

Several techniques for analyzing text have been employed in Computational Linguistics,[1] including:

- **Decomposing a text using linguistic rhetorical predicates**: In her work on generation, McKeown (1985) used *rhetorical predicates* as defined by linguists (Williams, 1893; Shepherd, 1926; Grimes, 1975). McKeown defines rhetorical predicates as "the *means* which a speaker has for describing information. They characterize the different types of predicating acts he may use and they delineate the structural relations between propositions in a text." (McKeown, 1985: page 20). *Attributive* (providing an attribute) and *constituency* (description of subparts or subtypes) are examples of such predicates. A text is decomposed by assigning a predicate to each proposition. Standard patterns of discourse are then sought by identifying whether some combinations of predicates are more likely to occur than others, and whether a specific combination is more frequent for a given discourse situation (such as *providing a definition*, or *comparing and contrasting two entities*).

- **Decomposing a text using coherence relations**: *Coherence relations* indicate how spans of text relate to each other. There are two main theories of discourse structure that make use of such relations:

  - Hobbs' theory of *coherence relations* (Hobbs 1978; 1979; 1985): In attempting to formalize the notion of coherence in a discourse and decide what makes a discourse coherent, Hobbs identified relations that relate the *current utterance* to the *previous discourse*. According to Hobbs, a speaker must decide in which way to expand the previous discourse segment in constructing a text (or discourse). This decision is reflected in the

---

[1] Researchers in Linguistics have also used slightly different methods for analyzing texts , e.g., Hasan (1978, 1979), van Dijk (1980), Ventola (1983, 1984), and O'Donnell (1990). We have chosen the ones mentioned above as they currently lend themselves the best for computational implementation of generation systems, because of the specificity of their definitions.

coherence relation that connects the new sentence to the previous utterances. For example, if a speaker needs to connect new information with what is already known by the hearer, the speaker chooses one of the *linkage relations*, such as *background* or *explanation*. As another example, when a speaker wishes to move between specific and general statements, he or she must employ one of the *expansion relations*, such as *elaboration* relation or *generalization*. From the hearer's perspective, understanding why the speaker continued as he or she did is equivalent to determining what relation was used. For text analysis, a text can be decomposed by noting which coherence relations hold between a new sentence and the previous text.

– Rhetorical Structure Theory (RST) (Mann, 1984; Mann and Thompson, 1987; Mann and Thompson, 1988): In another attempt to formalize the notion of coherence, Mann and Thompson identified a set of approximately 25 relations (RST *relations* (e.g., *motivation*, *evidence*, or *circumstance*) that may exist between adjacent spans in a coherent English text. Using these relations, a text is decomposed into segments which include a *nucleus* and one or more *satellites*. The nucleus segment is the main focus of the text, while the satellite usually supports the claim given in the nucleus segment and is connected to the nucleus with one of the relations. Together, the nucleus and the satellite accomplish a goal the writer/speaker has in mind. Like Hobbs' coherence relations, these relations reflect a communicative goal the speaker is trying to achieve. At the time of this research, the definition of these relations were mostly descriptive.

In this work, although we began by analyzing our texts using these various methods to compare the text's organizational structures, we finally adopted the first method, i.e., decomposing the texts with rhetorical predicates, as was done in McKeown (1985). We in fact employed the same set of rhetorical predicates. Our aim was to find consistent groupings of predicates in each group of texts and formalize these structures as discourse strategies to guide the generation process. We chose rhetorical predicates because their definition was specific enough to be readily applicable to define strategies for text generation, and had indeed already been successfully applied in computer systems – e.g., (McKeown, 1985; McCoy, 1986). On the other hand, coherence relations had mainly been used in language interpretation, e.g., to predict what kinds of anaphora can occur. But, as many different coherence relations can be chosen at any point during the discourse construction, depending on the speaker's goals, it was hard to use these coherence relations for text generation without further constraints on how the relations should be arranged. Similarly, RST relations were mainly descriptive at this point, and much work needed to be done to operationalize them for generation (Hovy, 1988b; Moore and Paris, 1989; Moore and Paris, 1992b). (This will be discussed further in Chapter 8.)

3.2 The texts analyzed

To develop effective strategies for tailoring a description to a particular level of expertise, we selected descriptions from a variety of naturally occurring texts: adult encyclopedias (Britannica, 1964; Collier, 1962), junior encyclopedias (Britannica-Junior, 1963; New Book of Knowledge, 1967; Encyclopedia of Science, 1982), manuals (Chevrolet, 1978; Weissler and Weissler, 1973) and high school text books – e.g., (Baker *et al.*, 1957; Verwiebe *et al.*, 1962). These texts were chosen because they provide a good source of descriptions, and because they seem to address audiences at the two ends of the knowledge spectrum: naive and expert. Texts from adult encyclopedias are directed at an audience much more knowledgeable in general than the audience addressed by high school text books and junior encyclopedias. Likewise, the Chevrolet repair manual is aimed at knowledgeable users (professional mechanics) while the other manual, (Weissler and Weissler, 1973), claims to be directed towards novices. These texts thus constitute a good starting point for studying the differences between the descriptions given to naive users and those given to experts in a domain.

We studied descriptions of devices, taking the description of the same object in all sources whenever possible. This allows for good comparisons of the texts, both in terms of content and organization. To minimize the effects of stylistic differences on our results, texts from at least two different encyclopedias in each audience category were chosen. We examined about fifteen examples from each encyclopedia and textbook and a few from the manuals. The descriptions studied were generally several paragraphs in length.

Given the desire to focus on how a reader's assumed domain knowledge can affect a description, encyclopedia texts have an added advantage besides providing examples of descriptions. They are directed to a general audience and people turning to them do so for a variety of reasons. Yet, they all read the same texts and thus acquire the same information, regardless of their goal for reading these texts. Encyclopedia texts are not directly aimed to help achieve particular goals. Rather, they provide general information intended to be useful to achieve any goal a reader may have. Thus an encyclopedia must provide its readers with some information about an object, without knowing or attempting to address a reader's specific goals. This property of encyclopedias gives us the opportunity to focus on how the *level of expertise* affects a description, without considering how the goals and specific beliefs of the reader could affect it. A sophisticated text generation system should of course take all these user's characteristics into consideration in order to construct a text, and it is necessary to study how these characteristics affect each other. However, understanding these factors separately first will help us study their interaction later. In this work, being more concerned with the role played by the user's domain knowledge, we simply assume that users want descriptions that allow them to build functional models of the object.

3.2.1 The textual analysis

Following McKeown's approach, the texts were decomposed into different propositions (or clauses), and each proposition was classified as a type of predicate. The predicates were taken from (McKeown, 1985). They are based on Williams, Grimes and Shepherd's definitions (Williams, 1893; Shepherd, 1926; Grimes, 1975). The predicates employed in our analysis are shown in Figure 3.1.[2] We have to note that, as pointed out in both McKeown (1985) and Mann and Thompson (1987, 1988), this type of analysis (decomposing the text into rhetorical predicates, rhetorical relations, or any such structure) is somewhat subjective, as there are no precise criteria for determining the function of each proposition: this is determined by the researcher performing the analysis, and he or she labels the proposition with a predicate. Furthermore, in some cases, propositions cannot be clearly assigned to a single predicate. In other cases, a clause might combine information from two predicates. This will be illustrated later.

The analysis showed that the texts fell into two groups: most of the descriptions in the adult encyclopedia entries and in the car manual for mechanics were organized around object subparts and their properties, while the descriptions in the junior encyclopedia entries and in the car manual for novices traced process information, i.e., these descriptions provided an explanation of how the object performed its function.

Consider for example the descriptions of filament lamps shown in Figure 3.2. The first text in this figure is from *Collier's Encyclopedia* and the second from the *New Book of Knowledge (The Children's Encyclopedia)*. In the first sentence of the text for adult readers, the parts of the filament lamp are immediately introduced, with some attributes, and the text concentrates on providing the parts of the filament lamp. In the text for the junior audience, after an prefatory sentence to introduce the term "filament lamp," the author explains what happens in a lamp. Only one part gets explicitly mentioned as part of this explanation ("a thread"), and the description concentrates on *process information*.

These texts are typical of those found in the different sets of sources. The main difference between these two types of descriptions is in the *kinds of information* they provide (details about *parts* versus details about *processes*), although there are also some differences in the surface structure (that is, the vocabulary and syntax used). As the main concern of this work is in deciding what to include in a text and how to organize the facts coherently, the differences in syntactic structure and vocabulary will not be addressed here. They will be briefly discussed in Chapter 8.

Since these two types of descriptions were found in text, a system that generates device descriptions should also be able to provide these different kinds of descriptions appropriately. Based on our data, we postulate that the assumed level of expertise of the intended reader affects the choice of strategy. There is thus another dimension along which a system can tailor its answers to a user's level of domain knowledge: instead of simply varying the *amount of detail* provided, a system can also vary the *kind of information* contained in a text.

---

[2]See (McKeown, 1985, pages 20–24) for a more complete discussion of these predicates.

1. *Identification*: Description of an object in terms of its superordinate.
   Example: This bear is a panda bear.

2. *Constituency*: Description of the subparts or subentities.
   Example: The telephone consists of a transmitter, a receiver and a housing.

3. *Attributive*: Associating properties with an entity.
   Example: Beth's teddy bear is black and white.

4. *Cause-effect*: A cause-effect relationship between two events or relations.
   Example: The soundwaves strike the diaphragm and cause it to vibrate.

5. *Analogy*: The making of an analogy.
   Example: The X-ray tube is very similar to the cathode ray tubes you have been studying except that the electron beam is aimed at a metal target instead of a glass screen.

6. *Renaming*: Providing an alternative name for an entity.
   Example: The current goes through the coil, called the 'primary coil'.

7. *Comparison*: Comparing an entity/event to another entity/event
   Example: The diaphragm vibrates in just the same way the molecules of air are vibrating

Figure 3.1: Rhetorical predicates used in this analysis

from *Collier's Encyclopedia (1962)*, an adult encyclopedia

Typical household incandescent lamps (general service) are constructed with the following parts: a coiled tungsten filament, a glass bulb to keep air out and inert gases in, and a base that serves as a holding device and connects the filament to the electric supply. These three parts vary in size and shapes with each different class of lamps, such as general service, reflector, showcase, street-lighting, automobile sealed beam, miniature flash lights and photograph lamps.

from the *New Book of Knowledge (1967)*, a junior encyclopedia

The type of electric lamp made by Edison is called a filament lamp. A filament lamp lights when a thread inside it heats up to incandescence - that is when it heats so brightly that it gleams with light.

Figure 3.2: Two descriptions of the filament lamps

To be able to generate these two types of descriptions, it is necessary to formalize their different organizational structures. The difference between the two kinds of texts is captured in terms of two distinct discourse strategies: the *constituency schema* and the *process trace*.

3.2.2   Analyses of entries from adult encyclopedias and the car manual for experts

The texts from the adult encyclopedias and the Chevrolet manual can be characterized in terms of the *constituency schema*, a discourse strategy posited in (McKeown, 1985). These texts essentially provide details about the parts of an object and their properties (attributes).

In McKeown's analysis, the constituency schema was associated with the discourse goals of providing definitions and describing available information. This is also the goal TAILOR has when providing a description. Like other strategies that have been proposed thus far, the constituency schema is an abstract characterization of patterns occurring frequently in texts. A text generated using this strategy will reflect this pattern, and will not be primarily dependent on the underlying knowledge base from which the facts are drawn. We term such strategies *declarative strategies*. Although the generated text is dependent on the knowledge base to the extent that the text can only contain facts included in the knowledge base, the structure of the text reflects more the abstract pattern embodied in the declarative strategy than the structure of the knowledge base.

1. {Identify the object as a member of some generic class, using the *identification* predicate}

2. Present the constituents of the item to be defined (subparts or sub-entities). This corresponds to the *constituency* predicate

3. Present characteristic information about each constituent in turn. This corresponds to the *depth-attributive* predicate

4. {Present additional information about the item to be defined. This corresponds to the *attributive* predicate}

Figure 3.3: The constituency schema

The constituency schema, which will be presented formally in the next chapter, can be characterized by the four steps indicated in Figure 3.3.[3] Some of these predicates can be expanded into a schema, resulting in the recursive use of the schema. For example, instead of using the *depth-attributive* predicate, which means providing information about the subparts of an object, it is possible to use the constituency schema (or the attributive schema) recursively to provide more details about each part.

As an example of a text whose structure matches the constituency schema, consider the text shown in Figure 3.4. This description of a telephone is taken from *Collier's Encyclopedia*. In the first sentence, the telephone is described in terms of its subparts: the transmitter, the receiver and the housing. This proposition corresponds to the constituency predicate, the second step of the schema. The first step of the schema, identification in terms of a generic class, was omitted. Following this sentence, the two main subparts are described in turn: the transmitter, in sentences 2 through 8 and the receiver in sentences 9 to 13. In this text, both parts are described in detail with a recursive call of the schema instead of one predicate, and depth-attributive information includes the use of both the constituency and attributive predicates.

For example, depth-attributive information about the transmitter is included in sentences 2 to 8. In (2), an attribute of the "diaphragm" is given, here a structural relation (e.g., "the diaphragm is clamped"), followed by a cause-effect relation in (3) that justifies the attribute provided in (2) (e.g., "it is clamped *to improve the high frequency response*"). In (4), more attributive information about the diaphragm is presented, still a structural relation, introducing a new subpart, the "doubly-resonant system," followed by a functional relation (which might also be considered a cause-effect relation) in (6). The components of the newly introduced part, the doubly-resonant system, were also immediately introduced in (5) (e.g. "a cavity and an air-chamber").

Note that, sometimes, two predicates are combined in the surface structure into one

---

[3] The steps included in curly brackets are optional.

Text	Predicates
1) The hand-sets introduced in 1947 consist of a receiver and a transmitter in a single housing available in black or colored plastic.	*Constituency (with attributive)*
	Depth-Attributive for the transmitter:
2) The transmitter diaphragm is clamped rigidly at its edges	*Attributive*
3) to improve the high frequency response.	*Cause-effect*
4) The diaphragm is coupled to a doubly resonant system	*Attributive*
5) – a cavity and an air chamber –	*Constituency*
6) which broadens the response.	*Attributive*
7) The carbon chamber contains carbon granules,	*Constituency*
8) the contact resistance of which is varied by the diaphragm's vibration.	*Attributive / Cause-effect*
	Depth-Attributive for the receiver:
9) The receiver includes a ring-shaped magnet system around a coil and a ring shaped armature of anadium Permendur.	*Constituency (with attributive)*
10) Current in the coil makes the armature vibrate in the air gap.	*Cause-effect*
11) An attached phenolic-impregnated fabric diaphragm,	*Attributive*
12) shaped like a dome,	*Attributive*
13) vibrates and sets the air in the canal of the ear in motion.	*Cause-effect*

Figure 3.4: Description of a telephone from an adult encyclopedia

clause. As an example, the first sentence clearly corresponds to the constituency predicate, as the parts or constituents of the telephone are given. A strict categorization would, however, decompose this sentence into first the constituency predicate, corresponding to the listing of the parts, and then the depth-attributive predicate, since attributes (properties) of the "housing" are provided: "available in black or colored plastic." The two predicates were then merged in the surface structure. The same information could have been conveyed using two sentences: one using the constituency followed by another using the attributive predicate to further describe the housing, as in: "The hand-sets consist of a receiver, a transmitter and a housing. The housing is available in black or colored plastic." Immediately including properties results in a more concise text, however. A similar phenomenon appears in (9), where the magnet is described as being "ring-shaped" and "around a coil," and the armature as being "ring shaped" and made of "anadium Permendur."

This effect can be achieved with a sophisticated surface generator capable of merging two predicates into a sentence when appropriate. Although TAILOR does not have such an elaborate surface generator, it is able to mimic this behavior in the implementation of the *predicate semantics*, that is the functions that retrieve information corresponding to the predicates from the knowledge base. To mimic this behavior, the functions can retrieve more information from the knowledge base than strictly required by the predicates. In other words, instead of merging two predicates at the surface structure level, the program will anticipate the use of two predicates one after the other and immediately retrieve the information for both. For example, in TAILOR's implementation, the semantics of the constituency predicate allow mentioning the parts together with several properties. This is in anticipation that the depth-attributive predicate (that can retrieve properties) will be chosen after the constituency predicate. This feature will be described in more detail in Chapter 6, where TAILOR's implementation is presented.

Another example of a description from an adult encyclopedia, shown in Figure 3.5, is a description of transformers from the *Encyclopedia Britannica*. The transformer is first identified as a member of a super class: "inductors." This corresponds to the identification predicate, the first step of the schema. Identification here also includes the functionality. A description of the transformer's parts follows: first the parts are given ("two or more windings"), and depth-attributive information about the windings is provided in (5). The description then returns to the top level object being described, the transformer, and the paragraph ends by presenting properties associated with transformers. Two causal links are presented in this description. Instead of explaining how transformers function, however, these links serve as justification for a property that was just given. For example, the cause-effect relation included in sentence (9), "to minimize energy losses," justifies the property presented in sentence (8), "is laminated," but does not explain how transformers transform alternating current.

The descriptions presented above, like the lamp description from the adult encyclopedia presented in Figure 3.2, are organized around the subparts and attributive information of the objects being defined, even though a causal link is occasionally presented. Attributive information includes spatial and structural relations, as in "the diaphragm is coupled to a doubly resonant system," and properties, as in "shaped like a dome."

Text	Predicates
1) Transformers are special forms of inductors widely used in electronics	*Identification*
2) to transform alternating power to one or more circuits at the same frequency, but usually with changed values of voltage and current.	*Cause-Effect (Function)*
3) They operate on the principle of electronic induction.	*Attributive*
4) All transformers consist of two or more windings	*Constituency*
5) so arranged that a change of flux in one winding induces a change of flux in the other.	*Attributive*
6) They are usually provided with a high-permeability material.	*Attributive*
7) to increase the efficiency of the flux linkage and	*Cause-Effect*
8) this material is laminated or otherwise divided	*Attributive*
9) to minimize the energy losses that would occur in solid material.	*Cause-Effect*

Figure 3.5: Description of transformers from an adult encyclopedia

When functional information is provided, it serves as a justification of a property just mentioned. For example, the causal link "to improve the high frequency response" in the description of the telephone (in Figure 3.4) elaborates on the structural relation "the diaphragm is clamped" and justifies this relation; it does not really explain the mechanism of the telephone.

3.2.3 Texts from junior encyclopedias, high school textbooks, and the car manual for novices

While most of the texts from the adult encyclopedias and the Chevrolet car manual can be characterized using the constituency schema, texts from the junior encyclopedias, high school textbooks and the car manual for novices could not be described by any known schema or other organizing structure. Moreover, identifying the rhetorical predicates of the sentences did not provide insights to a useful organizing structure. As we will show in the examples, the structure resulting from using rhetorical predicates is one that contains mainly cause-effect predicates. Although this structure is a simple schema, it is not useful for generation as it does not provide enough constraints in deciding what to include in a text.

In looking for other types of organizing strategies, we discovered that the main strategy used in these descriptions was to trace through the processes that allow the object to perform its function. We termed this strategy the *process trace* and have developed a precise formulation, consisting of *directives*, or instructions, rather than predicates. This strategy is not an abstract pattern formed of rhetorical predicates, as is the constituency schema. Instead, the strategy is more like an algorithm that follows the underlying knowledge base very closely and gives directives on how to trace it to provide a causal description of the object. We term this type of strategy a *procedural* strategy.

As an example, consider the description of the telephone in Figure 3.6, taken from the *Britannica Junior Encyclopedia* (1983). In this description, the author starts by explaining what happens when someone speaks into a telephone, sentence (1), and why a diaphragm located inside the transmitter vibrates (3). While introducing the diaphragm as part of a causal link, the author also includes properties about the diaphragm: it is "aluminum" and "disc-shaped." Now that the diaphragm has been introduced as part of the process, it is described more fully in sentences (5) through (9) with various properties and structural relations. The description then reverts to tracing the process information, explaining how the soundwaves are transformed into varying current and describing how the telephone achieves its function of transmitting soundwaves.

As the vibration process in (3) can be decomposed into two substeps (i.e., "the diaphragm moves inward" and "the diaphragm springs back"), the author traces each one in turn (sentences (11) through (13) for the first substep, and (14) through (16) for the second). Sentence (17) summarizes these substeps, also indicating that the process trace will now continue at the top level, not the substep level. Sentence (18) continues the process trace by describing where current flows next.

In the remaining text, the author explains how the varying current is changed back into soundwaves in the receiver of the telephone. Again, the author traces through substeps when a process step can be divided: "the current strength varying" can be divided into the "current becomes stronger", sentence (20), and "the current becomes weaker" (21). Each substep is traced in turn. The text organization for this description is summarized in Figures 3.7 and 3.8.

The organizing principle of this text is the mechanical process underlying the function of the telephone. The decomposition of the text into predicates, as shown in the second column in Figure 3.6, emphasizes that the text is *primarily*, although not exclusively, formed of causal links. In this text, the process description gets interrupted when descriptive information can be included about a subpart that was just mentioned as part of the process description. For example, attributive information about the diaphragm was provided after the diaphragm was introduced in the causal links. Furthermore, not only is the description made mainly through a process trace, but this process trace can be given in great detail by explaining substeps if there are any. The information contained in a description aimed at naive users corresponds to the causal links that connect the various processes contained in the knowledge base that explains how the object performs its function.

As another example, the description of transformers from the *Britannica Junior Encyclopedia* is shown in Figure 3.9. In this description, the author first explains the principle behind a transformer's mechanism in sentences (1) through (3). (This mechanism description also makes use of the *renaming* predicate twice: *called the 'primary coil'* and *or 'secondary coil'*.). This causal explanation forms the emphasis of the

Text	Predicates
1) When one speaks into the transmitter of a modern telephone, the sound waves strike against an aluminum disk	*Cause-effect*
2) or diaphragm	*Renaming*
3) and cause it to vibrate back and forth	*Cause-effect*
4) in just the same way the molecules of air are vibrating.	*Comparison between two actions*
5) The center of this diaphragm is connected with the carbon button	*Attributive*
6) originally invented by Thomas A. Edison.	*Attributive*
7) This is a little brass box filled with granules of carbon	*Attributive*
8) composed of especially selected and treated coal.	*Attributive*
9) The front and back of the button are insulated.	*Attributive*
10) The talking current is passed through this box so that the electricity must find its way from granule to granule inside the box.	*Cause-effect*
11) When the diaphragm moves inward under the pressure from the sound waves the carbon grains are pushed together	*Cause-effect*
12) and the electricity finds an easier path.	*Cause-effect*
13) Thus a strong current flows through the line.	*Cause-effect*
14) When a thin portion of the sound waves comes along, the diaphragm springs back,	*Cause-effect*
15) allowing the carbon particles to be more loosely packed, and	*Cause-effect*
16) consequently less current can find its way through.	*Cause-effect*
17) So a varying or undulating current is sent over the line whose vibrations exactly correspond to the vibrations caused by the speaker's voice.	*Cause-effect between two actions*
18) This current then flows through the line to the coils of an electromagnet in the receiver.	*Cause-effect*
19) Very near to the poles of this magnet is a thin iron disc.	*Attributive*
20) When the current becomes stronger it pulls the disc toward it.	*Cause-effect*
21) As a weaker current flows through the magnet, it is not strong enough to attract the disk and it springs back.	*Cause-effect*
22) Thus the diaphragm in the receiver is made to vibrate in and out....	*Cause-effect*

Figure 3.6: Description of a telephone from a junior encyclopedia

Text	Structure

1) When one speaks into the transmitter of a modern telephone, the sound waves strike against an aluminum disk 2) or diaphragm and 3) cause it to vibrate back and forth 4) in just the same way the molecules of air are vibrating.	Process trace at top level:
	one speaks
	  → *soundwaves strike diaphragm*
	  → *diaphragm vibrates*

5) The center of this diaphragm is connected with the carbon button 6) originally invented by Thomas A. Edison.	Attributive information about the diaphragm, a part just introduced during the process trace.
7) This is a little brass box filled with granules of carbon 8) composed of especially selected and treated coal. 9) The front and back of the button are insulated.	Attributive information about the button.
10) The talking current is passed through this box so that the electricity must find its way from granule to granule inside the box.	Process at top level: *current flows through the box*

	Diaphragm vibrates can be decomposed into two substeps:
	  - diaphragm moves inward
	  - diaphragm springs back

11) When the diaphragm moves inward under the pressure from the sound waves the carbon grains are pushed together and 12) the electricity finds an easier path. 13) Thus a strong current flows through the line.	Process trace for the first substep:
	diaphragm moves inward
	  → *carbon grains pushed*
	    together
	    → *more current*

14) When a thin portion of the sound wave comes along, the diaphragm springs back, 15) allowing the carbon particles to be more loosely packed, and 16) consequently less current can find its way through.	Process trace for the second substep:
	diaphragm springs back
	  → *carbon grains looser*
	  → *less current*

17) So a varying or undulating current is sent over the line whose vibrations exactly correspond to the vibrations caused by the speaker's voice.	Summary; Back to tracing process at top level.

Figure 3.7: Organization of the description of the telephone from a Junior Encyclopedia

Text	Structure
18) This current then flows through the line to the coils of an electromagnet in the receiver.	Process trace at top level
19) Very near to the poles of this magnet is a thin iron disc.	Attributive information about the magnet.
	Again, there are two substeps: - current increasing - current decreasing
20) When the current becomes stronger it pulls the disc toward it.	Process trace for the first substep: *current increases → disc is pulled*
21) As a weaker current flows through the magnet, it is not strong enough to attract the disk and it springs back.	Process trace for the second substep: *current decreases → disc is released*
22) Thus the diaphragm in the receiver is made to vibrate in and out....	Summary.

Figure 3.8: Organization of the description of the telephone from a Junior Encyclopedia – Cont'd.

1) If two coils of wire are properly arranged close to one another, they will make a transformer. 2) When an alternating current is sent through one of the coils, called the 'primary coil', an alternating current will be created, or induced, in the second or 'secondary coil'. 3) The voltage of the current in each coil depends on the number of turns of wire around the coil. 4) For example, if the primary coil has 100 turns and secondary coil has 500 turns, the voltage of the current in the secondary coil will be five times as great as the voltage of the current in the primary coil. 5) Such a transformer is called a 'step-up' transformer. 6) By winding fewer turns of wire around the secondary coil, the voltage is decreased. 7) This makes a 'step-down' transformer. 8) The primary and secondary coils of transformers for power circuits are wound around an iron core. 9) The "iron" in the core is actually many layers of thin steel strips. 10) The same core serves for both windings. 11) Thin strips are used because magnetism can not change rapidly in a solid iron core and also because a solid core would be heated by the magnetism.

Figure 3.9: Description of transformers from a junior encyclopedia

description. The description continues with two illustrating examples in sentences (4) through (7), which still refers to the function of the transformer. Finally, after the parts (the coils) have been introduced, their properties are presented in sentences (8) through (11).

The theme of the texts from this group is the description of the function and the mechanical processes associated with the object being described. In this type of description, the object is mainly described in terms of the *functions* performed by its subparts in order to explain how the object achieves its purpose. The description traces through the process information instead of enumerating the object's subparts along with their attributes, as was the case in the descriptions matching the constituency schema. The object's subparts are mentioned only when the description of the mechanical processes involves them. As a result, not all the subparts are mentioned. For example, in the description of a lamp from a junior encyclopedia (shown in Figure 3.2), the base was not mentioned. Similarly, in the description of the telephone (shown in Figure 3.6), the housing was left out. When a part is mentioned during the process trace, the process description sometimes gets interrupted to include descriptive information concerning that subpart.

In the texts for adults and experts, the description were organized around parts, and process information was included mainly as a justification or elaboration of a property (or a part) just mentioned, not as an explanation of the object's function. In the texts for the junior audience, the reverse is true: a part is mentioned only when it is involved in the process explanation, and information about parts is provided after a part has been introduced during the process trace. The description is constructed around process information. The preceding observations can be formalized in the definition of the process trace. This strategy, which is described in more detail in the next chapter, is summarized in Figure 3.10.[4]

This strategy is not an abstract pattern of predicates but rather an algorithm that dictates how to trace the knowledge base to provide a specific view on it, i.e., to provide a causal explanation.[5] Following this strategy, the emphasis of the description remains on the main path, that is the main sequence of events that take place when the object performs its function. This results in a coherent explanation of how the object performs its function. As indicated in step 3, it is possible to provide more information about a subpart, once it has been introduced as part of the process trace, as was done in the two

---

[4]Curly brackets denotes optional steps.

[5]Other views could have been taken on this object, including a structural view as with the constituency schema. Yet other views include the types of explanations identified by (Stevens and Steinberg, 1981), such as "information flow", or "topological explanations". If these other views had to be produced, it is likely that other procedural strategies would have to be defined. The process trace as described here is analogous to what Stevens and Steinberg call a physical-causal explanation. Note also that what we call here *process descriptions* are similar to the types of text generated by the STEAMER program (Hollan *et al.*, 1984). This is not surprising as STEAMER was designed to *explain the process* of a steamer. In STEAMER, however, texts – and graphics – were canned, and STEAMER did *not* reason about what to present. This is a major difference with our system. Furthermore, part of the importance of the process description in our case lies in the fact that it is *one* way of describing an object, which could also have been described in a very structural way in a different context. Our system must thus reason about when to use which type of strategy, and it must select the appropriate information from the knowledge base.

1. Find the *main path*, that is the main sequence of events that take place when the object performs its function. (We will explain in the next chapter how the main path can be obtained.)

   Starting from the first event in this sequence:

2. Follow the next causal link on the main path.

3. {Give attributive information about a subpart just introduced}

4. {Include a side link, that is a link not on the main path, though related to it}

5. {Follow the substeps if there are any}

6. Go Back to (2).

Figure 3.10: The process trace algorithm

examples presented in this section. As will be explained in Chapter 5, this step of the strategy can be replaced by a call to the constituency schema for a subpart, if a fuller structural description is desired. In step 4, it is possible to include a side link, that is a link that is not on the main path. This will be discussed in the next chapter. Finally, when a step can be divided into substeps, the causal explanation can be continued at the substep level, as indicated in step 5. Substeps happen, for example, in the following case: the step " ... causes the diaphragm to vibrate" can be divided into the two substeps: "the diaphragm moves inward" and "the diaphragm moves outward." In the description of the telephone, the causal explanation continued at the substep level. Substeps can also arise when a complex object is made of several other complex parts.

Substeps can be followed either when a decomposable step is encountered (as in the description of the telephone), or after traversing the main path entirely. The latter appears desirable when there are many substeps, each leading to a long sequence of events, to avoid distracting the reader's attention from the main path for a long period. It also seems more desirable when the substeps arise because a subpart itself has process information associated with it. In that case, first an explanation of how the object parts work together to achieve the object's function is given. Then, if a long description is desired, it is possible to step through each of the parts, describing how it achieves its own function. This is similar to the schema recursion for the constituency schema in (McKeown, 1985). Figure 3.11[6] illustrates how including a long subpart's process explanation while still explaining the top level object's function might be confusing as it might distract from the top-level object's process information. Figure 3.12[7] shows

---

[6] This text was formed by inserting the description of a microphone into the description of a tape recorder taken from the *New Encyclopedia of Science* (Encyclopedia of Science, 1982).

[7] This text was formed by inserting the description of a microphone after the description of a tape recorder taken from the *New Encyclopedia of Science* (Encyclopedia of Science, 1982).

Description of a tape recorder

The tape recorder is a machine that records, stores, and reproduces sound. A tape recorder has a microphone which picks up sounds. The microphone changes sounds into electric currents. *The microphone converts soundwaves into current. When a person speaks into a microphone, the soundwaves strike against a diaphragm and cause it to vibrate back and forth in just the same way the molecules of air are vibrating. The talking current passes through a carbon chamber filled with granules, so that the electricity must find its way from granule to granule inside the box. When the diaphragm moves inward under the pressure from the soundwaves the carbon grains are pushed together and the electricity finds an easier path. Thus a strong current flows through the line. When a thin portion of the soundwaves comes along, the diaphragm springs back, allowing the carbon particles to be more loosely packed, and consequently less current can find its way through. So a varying or undulating current is sent over the line whose vibrations exactly correspond to the vibrations caused by the speaker's voice.* The electric currents go along a coil of wire which is wound round a metal bar, or core. When electricity flows in the wire, the metal core becomes a magnet. As soon as the electricity stops flowing, the core stops being a magnet. The metal core in the tape recorder becomes a magnet with each electric current from the microphone. This happens hundreds of times per second for most seconds. Every time the core becomes a magnet, it makes some of the particles on the tape into magnets. These particles remain magnets even after the tape has passed the core. They form a pattern on the tape. Different sounds produce different patterns. As the recording continues, the tape winds off one reel, or spool, onto another. Before the tape can be played back again, it must be wound onto the first spool again.

Figure 3.11: Including a subpart's process explanation while explaining the object's function

---

the description of the same object, with the subpart's process trace included after the main object's process trace. It is easier to understand the main path in that description. In both figures, the process information for the subpart is shown in italics.

3.2.4 Need for directives

In Figure 3.6, we showed the decomposition of the description of the telephone from a junior encyclopedia into rhetorical predicates. The text and its decomposition into rhetorical predicates is repeated in Figure 3.13. This decomposition helped determine that this text was mainly composed of causal links. However, the structure resulting from this decomposition is an introductory sentence followed by a pattern of cause-effect links, as can be seen in the figure. A schema can be formed from this decomposition, namely a schema comprising simply causal links.

Description of a tape recorder

The tape recorder is a machine that records, stores, and reproduces sound. A tape recorder has a microphone which picks up sounds. The microphone changes sounds into electric currents. The electric currents go along a coil of wire which is wound round a metal bar, or core. When electricity flows in the wire, the metal core becomes a magnet. As soon as the electricity stops flowing, the core stops being a magnet. The metal core in the tape recorder becomes a magnet with each electric current from the microphone. This happens hundreds of times per second for most seconds. Every time the core becomes a magnet, it makes some of the particles on the tape into magnets. These particles remain magnets even after the tape has passed the core. They form a pattern on the tape. Different sounds produce different patterns. As the recording continues, the tape winds off one reel, or spool, onto another. Before the tape can be played back again, it must be wound onto the first spool again.

The microphone converts soundwaves into current. When a person speaks into a microphone causes the soundwaves strike against a diaphragm and cause it to vibrate back and forth in just the same way the molecules of air are vibrating. The talking current passes through a carbon chamber filled with granules, so that the electricity must find its way from granule to granule inside the box. When the diaphragm moves inward under the pressure from the soundwaves the carbon grains are pushed together and the electricity finds an easier path. Thus a strong current flows through the line. When a thin portion of the soundwave comes along, the diaphragm springs back, allowing the carbon particles to be more loosely packed, and consequently less current can find its way through. So a varying or undulating current is sent over the line whose vibrations exactly correspond to the vibrations caused by the speaker's voice.

Figure 3.12: Including a subpart's process explanation after explaining the object's function

Description of a telephone from a junior encyclopedia

1) When one speaks into the transmitter of a modern telephone, the sound waves strike against an aluminum disk 2) or diaphragm 3) and cause it to vibrate back and forth 4) in just the same way the molecules of air are vibrating. 5) The center of this diaphragm is connected with the carbon button 6) originally invented by Thomas A. Edison. 7) This is a little brass box filled with granules of carbon 8) composed of especially selected and treated coal. 9) The front and back of the button are insulated. 10) The talking current is passed through this box so that the electricity must find its way from granule to granule inside the box. 11) When the diaphragm moves inward under the pressure from the sound waves the carbon grains are pushed together 12) and the electricity finds an easier path. 13) Thus a strong current flows through the line. 14) When a thin portion of the sound wave comes along, the diaphragm springs back, 15) allowing the carbon particles to be more loosely packed, and 16) consequently less current can find its way through. 17) So a varying or undulating current is sent over the line whose vibrations exactly correspond to the vibrations caused by the speaker's voice. 18) This current then flows through the line to the coils of an electromagnet in the receiver. 19) Very near to the poles of this magnet is a thin iron disc. 20) When the current becomes stronger it pulls the disc toward it. 21) As a weaker current flows through the magnet, it is not strong enough to attract the disk and it springs back. 22) Thus the diaphragm in the receiver is made to vibrate in and out....

Text Decomposition

1: Cause-effect	12: Cause-effect
2: Renaming	13: Cause-effect
3: Cause-effect	14: Cause-effect
4: Comparison	15: Cause-effect
5: Depth-Attributive	16: Cause-effect
6: Depth-Attributive	17: Cause-effect
7: Depth-attributive	18: Cause-effect
8: Depth-attributive	19: Depth-attributive
9: Depth-attributive	20: Cause-effect
10: Cause-effect	21: Cause-effect
11: Cause-effect	22: Cause-effect

Figure 3.13: Decomposition of the telephone example from the junior encyclopedia text into rhetorical predicates

Such a schema is not very useful as an organizing strategy for generation as it cannot sufficiently guide the generation system in its decision process. Indeed, there may be quite a few causal links in the knowledge base and such a schema does not help in choosing one over another or in choosing the links that will result in a coherent process explanation. There is thus a need for further directives that can guide the system in retrieving facts from the knowledge base.

It can be argued that the same holds for the constituency schema. Indeed, frequently, predicates will not sufficiently constrain the decision of what to include in the text. For example, the "identification" predicate may not totally constrain the superordinate. If an object has several superordinates, as in the case of multiple hierarchies, one would need further directives to decide on which superordinate to choose. For example, one might need to know the goal of the user in asking for a description in order to select the appropriate hierarchy, e.g., (McKeown *et al.*, 1985; Moore, 1989a). Alternatively, given a deep generalization tree, it might not always be adequate to provide the immediate superordinate to fill the identification predicate. With the "constituency", "attributive", and "example" predicates, a problem might arise when an object has too many parts, too many attributes, or can be illustrated with too many examples to include them all. Again, a priority scheme would have to decide which to include. This priority scheme might also consist of directives telling what to retrieve from the knowledge base after the initial choice based on the predicates is made. This situation only arises when the underlying knowledge base is very large and there are many choices for each predicate.

On the other hand, without directives on how to traverse the knowledge base, a system cannot determine which links to choose to provide a coherent causal description of an object, as there are different kinds of cause-effects links, and, moreover, there will be typically too many such links to include in the text. In this case, the predicates hardly constrain the decision process, and directives are immediately needed. This is why it is important to define a new strategy that consists of directives; this strategy, based on the underlying knowledge base, dictates which link to choose to form a process description.

Using the rhetorical predicates as in McKeown (1985) is not the only way to decompose a text in order to determine an organizing structure. As we mentioned earlier, another way to decompose a text that might give rise to a useful organizing structure is in terms of the *coherence relations* identified in (Hobbs, 1978; Hobbs, 1979; Hobbs, 1985). Figure 3.14 shows the decomposition of part of the description of the telephone from the *Britannica Junior Encyclopedia* (from Figure 3.6) in terms of coherence relations. These relations are useful to point out how the sentences in the text are related to the preceding text. Many different coherence relations can be chosen at any point during the discourse construction. As a result, to construct a coherent text from these relations, one would need to specify how they can be decomposed and in which order they should appear. Without these constraints, it would be hard to employ coherence relations to organize a text coherently when there are many choices in the knowledge base. The process trace provides these constraints.

Similarly, it is possible to obtain a decomposition of the texts using the RST *relations* by

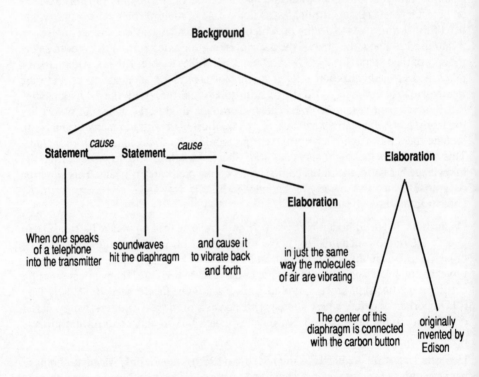

Figure 3.14: Decomposition of part of the telephone example from the junior encyclopedia text into coherence relations

Mann and Thomson (1987; 1988), also briefly described earlier. The decomposition of the telephone example from the junior encyclopedia using Mann and Thompson's rhetorical relations is shown in Figure 3.15. The pattern in this decomposition is one of *inform/elaboration-background* and *condition/conditional* nuclei, as shown in the figure. The elaboration and background, in the case of the junior encyclopedia texts, correspond to process information. Like the coherence relations, these relations do not restrict the textual order of the relations, and any schema can be expanded into any other at any point. Therefore, to use these schemata for generation and produce a clear process description, one would need a way to dictate which relation to include when. A control strategy must also determine which schema to expand, in which way to expand it, which satellite to choose, etc. Such a control strategy is precisely what the process strategy gives.

3.2.5   Summary of the textual analyses

There are (at least) two very different types of descriptions in naturally occurring texts that are characterized by means of distinct discourse strategies. One of these strategies, the process trace, is a new strategy that consists of directives instead of rhetorical predicates. These directives are necessary in order to sufficiently constrain the generation process. Identifying a new strategy is useful as the strategy can be added to the tools available to a generation system, thus increasing the kinds of texts that can be generated. This new strategy allows for the generation of process-oriented descriptions, as were found in the texts we examined.

As a result of the difference in organizing structures, the *type* of information that is included in the descriptions is also different: in the texts from the adult encyclopedias and the manual for experts, the information included is mainly structural, while in the texts from the junior encyclopedias and the manual for novices, the information included is mainly functional (or process oriented). One of the main differences between the two audiences at which the two groups of texts were aimed is their assumed level of domain knowledge. We postulate that the writers' choice of strategy might be based on the assumed domain knowledge of the expected readers.[8] If so, the reader's level of knowledge about the domain affects the *kind* of information provided as opposed to just the *amount* of information, as was previously assumed (Wallis and Shortliffe, 1982; Sleeman, 1982). This is significant as it adds a dimension (the different kinds of information available) along which a system can tailor its answers to users having different levels of domain knowledge. We will show in Chapters 5 and 6 how a user's level of expertise can be incorporated in a generation system and how it can guide the system in choosing a discourse strategy.

---

[8]No psychological experiments have been conducted to confirm this hypothesis. It is based on observations about what happens in natural texts.

1) When one speaks into the transmitter of a modern telephone, the sound waves strike against an aluminum disk 2) or diaphragm 3) and cause it to vibrate back and forth 4) in just the same way the molecules of air are vibrating. 5) The center of this diaphragm is connected with the carbon button 6) originally invented by Thomas A. Edison. 7) This is a little brass box filled with granules of carbon 8) composed of especially selected and treated coal. 9) The front and back of the button are insulated. 10) The talking current is passed through this box so that the electricity must find its way from granule to granule inside the box. 11) When the diaphragm moves inward under the pressure from the sound waves the carbon grains are pushed together 12) and the electricity finds an easier path. 13) Thus a strong current flows through the line. 14) When a thin portion of the sound wave comes along, the diaphragm springs back, 15) allowing the carbon particles to be more loosely packed, and 16) consequently less current can find its way through. 17) So a varying or undulating current is sent over the line whose vibrations exactly correspond to the vibrations caused by the speaker's voice. 18) This current then flows through the line to the coils of an electromagnet in the receiver. 19) Very near to the poles of this magnet is a thin iron disc. 20) When the current becomes stronger it pulls the disc toward it...

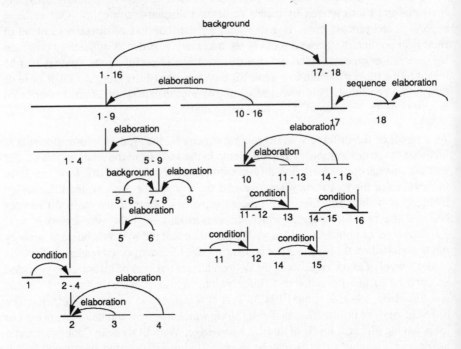

Figure 3.15: Decomposition of the telephone example from the junior encyclopedia text into nucleus/satellite schemata

3.2.6 Plausibility of this hypothesis

Recall that we assumed that the goal of a description is to allow the user to form a mental model of the functionality of the object. Research in psychology indicates that expert users have more knowledge not only about individual components but also about the causal models involved and the interconnections among parts, e.g. (Chi *et al.*, 1981; Lancaster and Kolodner, 1987). Expert users, then, are likely to have functional knowledge about the domain and to know how parts might interact with each other. As they can use this knowledge when reading the description,[9] they should be able to pull together all the parts provided in the description in order to "understand" the description as a whole. That is, they should be able to figure out how the parts fit together to form an object capable of performing a function. Since the reader is able to construct a mental model, it is unnecessary to include process information in the description. Assuming that the reader will be able to infer the processes involved, providing such information would contradict the principles of cooperative behavior (Grice, 1975).

On the other hand, a user who does not have enough knowledge to infer the processes linking the parts would be unlikely to understand a mostly structural description of an object and to be able to construct a functional mental model of the object from such a description. For this sort of naive user, if the description is to be informative and understandable, it must describe how the parts perform the function of the object. The description must therefore include process information. Previous research in reading comprehension also strengthens our belief that a user who does not have knowledge about the functions of the various parts will not be able to make sense of a description centered around parts (Davison, 1984; Wilson and Anderson, 1986). Criticizing readability formulas, Davison argues that these formulas often fail to correctly assess a text's difficulty because they do not measure the background knowledge a text requires in order to be understood; lack of background knowledge is often what makes a text hard to comprehend. Wilson and Anderson also point out that readers can fail to understand a text mainly because the text implicitly assumes knowledge that they do not have. A description that explicitly provides causal information might thus be appropriate for a naive user.

To summarize, we suggest that the user's domain knowledge should affect the content of a description with respect to the kind of information to include in a text, and not just the level of detail. We propose using the process trace when the user is relatively naive about the domain of discourse, and the constituency schema when the user has expertise about the domain. Extensive testing and thorough psychological experiments would be required to decide whether this is a good strategy choice. In any case, tailoring by changing the kind of information provided gives more flexibility in tailoring texts than was previously allowed for. Also, our analysis provides a further specification of the link between the user model and the generation process.

---

[9]Research in reading comprehension indicates that readers indeed use their previous knowledge in order to understand new texts (Schank and Abelson, 1977; Anderson *et al.*, 1977; Wilson and Anderson, 1986).

3.3 Combining the strategies for users with intermediate levels of expertise

The two strategies presented account for the main differences found between the adult and junior encyclopedia entries and can be used to describe objects to naive or expert users. Users are not necessarily either strictly naive or expert in a domain however. Users may have "local expertise" in that they may know about a few objects in the domain but not others (Paris, 1984). Such users would not be considered naive, but, as there are many objects they do not know in the domain, they would not be considered experts either. A combination of the two strategies presented for naive and expert users seems appropriate to describe objects to users with intermediate levels of expertise in order to provide them with the proper mix of structural and functional information.

As an example, suppose a description of a telephone is provided to a user who knows how a microphone works, but not how the telephone functions. In describing the telephone to this user it is necessary to first describe how the parts of the telephone work together, using the process trace strategy. It is not necessary, however, to describe the microphone using the process trace. Attributive information (or a call to the constituency schema) should be enough to describe the microphone. For the other part, the receiver, the process strategy is still appropriate in order to explain its mechanism.

Descriptions combining the two strategies occur in naturally occurring texts. Consider for example the text shown in Figure 3.16, taken from (Chemical, 1978). The description starts with the constituency schema but ends with a process trace, which is in italics in the figure: the "ir spectrometer" is first described in terms of its parts; each part is then described in turn (depth-attributive); finally, the authors switch to a process trace to describe the "thermocouple detector," probably assuming it is unknown to the reader. To fully understand this text, the reader must already know (or be able to infer information) about the ir spectrometer's purpose, the "ir radiation" and the "monochromator." We show how the strategies can be mixed in TAILOR in Chapter 5.

3.4 Summary

We analyzed texts from adult and junior encyclopedias, high school text books and manuals for experts and novices, in order to compare their organizing strategies. In doing so, we found that the entries from the adult encyclopedias and the manual for experts could be characterized by the *constituency schema*, a discourse strategy developed in (McKeown, 1985). These descriptions are organized around subparts and contain mainly details about subparts and their properties. On the other hand, the texts from junior encyclopedias, the high school text books and the manual for novices did not fit any known organizing strategy. We found that these descriptions tended to be organized around the process information associated with the objects being described, so that these descriptions contain more details about functional information. We called

52

IR spectrometer

(1) The ir spectrometer consists of three essential features: a source of ir radiation, a monochromator and a detector. (2) The primary sources of ir radiation are the Globar and Nernst glower. (3) The Globar is a silicon carbide rod heated to 1200 degrees C. (4) The Nerst glower is a rod containing a mixture of yttrium, zirconium, and erbium oxides that is heated electrically to 15000 degrees C. (5) Earlier ir spectrometers contained prism monochromators but today gratings are used almost exclusively. (6) Most detectors in modern spectrometers operate on the thermocouple principle. (7) Two dissimilar metal wires are connected to form a junction. *(8) Incident radiation causes a temperature rise at the junction and the difference in the temperature between head and tail causes a flow of current in the wires which is proportional to the intensity of the radiation.*

Text decomposition

1. Constituency
2-4. Depth attributive for the ir radiation
5. Depth attributive for the monochromators
6-7. Depth attributive for the detector
8. *Process trace for the thermocouple principle.*

Figure 3.16: Text from the *Encyclopedia of Chemical Technology*

---

this strategy the *process trace*. This is a new type of strategy in that it consists of directives on how to trace the knowledge base rather than of rhetorical predicates. The differences in organizing strategies in these two categories of descriptions are important as we are thus able to provide a further specification of how the user model affects the generation process. Furthermore, this result adds a new dimension along which tailoring a description to the user's level of expertise can be done.

Chapter 4

The discourse strategies used in TAILOR

In the previous chapter, we have shown that there were two distinct discourse strategies to generate descriptions of complex devices, depending on the user's level of expertise: the constituency schema for users knowledgeable about the domain, and the process trace for naive users. A description using the constituency schema is organized around the properties and parts of the object being described. The process trace revolves around the processes allowing the object to perform its function. In this chapter, each strategy is presented in detail.

4.1 Constituency Schema

The constituency strategy was described by McKeown (1985). It is a declarative strategy as it represents an abstract characterization of patterns occurring in many texts. As the strategy has been presented at length in (McKeown, 1985), it is discussed only briefly, and the change that was made to adapt it to TAILOR is described.

The constituency schema, as identified by McKeown, is represented formally in terms of its rhetorical predicates in Figure 4.1 below, using McKeown's notation: "{}" indicates optionality,"/" indicates alternatives, "+" indicates that the item may appear 1-n times, "*" indicates that the item may appear 0-n times, and ";" is used to indicate that it was not possible to unambiguously classify the propositions appearing in the text as one predicate.

Constituency (description of subparts or subtypes.)
Attributive* (associating properties with an entity) / Cause-effect*/
{ Depth-identification / Depth-attributive
    { Particular Illustration / Evidence}
    { Comparison ; Analogy}   }+
{ Attributive / Explanation / Amplification / Analogy }

Example from (McKeown, 1985)

Steam and electric torpedoes. 1) Modern torpedoes are of 2 general types. 2) Steam-propelled models have speeds of 27 to 45 knots and range of 4000 to 25,000 yds.. (4,367 - 27,350 meters). 3) The electric powered models are similar 4) but do not leave the telltale wake created by the exhaust of a steam torpedo.

Text decomposition

1. Constituency (subtypes)
2. Depth-identification (attributive)
3. Comparison
4. Depth-identification (attributive)

Figure 4.1: The Constituency Schema as defined by McKeown (1985)

Following this strategy, an object is first described in terms of its subparts or subtypes. Then, the description can proceed either by providing attributive information about the object being described, or by switching to the subparts (or subtypes), using the depth-attributive or depth-identification predicate. Finally, more attributive information might be presented about the original object being described.

TAILOR uses a slightly altered version of McKeown's schema. It includes the identification predicate and the attributive predicate at the beginning of the schema, as, in the texts analyzed, objects were very often first identified in terms of a superordinate, often together with functional information (such as the purpose of the object) or attributive information. These predicates are optional, however. This was the only change that needed to be performed, as the texts examined matched the rest of the constituency schema as defined. The resulting schema, together with an example, is shown in Figure 4.2.[1]

4.2   Process Trace

The process trace dictates how to traverse the knowledge base in order to describe the mechanisms that allow a device to perform its function. A description following a process trace thus explains a device's mechanism. Based on our data, even a causal description starts by introducing the object. As a result, the first step of the process trace is also to identify a device in terms of its superordinate, together with a summary of its function if possible. This step is thus similar to the first step of the constituency schema . After this prefatory sentence, the device's mechanism is explained. This is the main part of the process trace, and it is the part that is described in detail in this chapter.

The process trace can be seen as following a sequence of events, called the *main path* going from a *start* state to a *goal* state. In a device description, this chain of events describes how the object performs its function, from the beginning (start state) to the end (goal state), thus providing an explanation of that process.

To use the process trace, the main path of links from the start to the goal must be identified. Given the main path, the strategy then decides what to include in the description as the program traces along the path. A link that is not on the main path but that is attached to it (that is, a link relating an event *on* the main path to an event *not* on the main path) is termed a *side link*. A *series* of events that is either coming off the main path (i.e., whose *first event* is on the main path) or whose *last event* is on the main path is termed a *side chain*. When an event can be decomposed into another series of events, these events are called *substeps*. The process trace makes decisions about which link to include based on the type of side links, side chains or substeps it encounters. These decisions are explained later in this chapter.

---

[1] Note, however, that as McKeown had done in the TEXT system (McKeown, 1985), we did not implement all the predicates in TAILOR, as not all were supported by the knowledge base.

{Identification (description of an object in terms of its superordinate)}
{Attributive}*
Constituency (description of subparts or subtypes.)
Attributive* (associating properties with an entity) / Cause-effect* /
{ Depth-identification / Depth-attributive
    { Particular Illustration / Evidence}
    { Comparison ; Analogy }   }$^+$
{ Attributive / Explanation / Amplification / Analogy }

Text: Abacus (Collier, 1962):	**Predicates**
1) An abacus is a manually operated storage device that aids a human operator.	*Identification*
2) It consists of a row of any number of parallel wires, rods and grooves	*Constituency*
3) on or in which slide small beads or blocks.	*Depth-Attributive*
4) The strung beads are divided into two sections by means of a bar perpendicular to the rods.	*Depth-Attributive*
5) One section has one or two beads, representing 0 and 5, depending on their position along the rod.	*Depth-Attributive*
6) The second section has four or five beads, representing units.	*Depth-Attributive*
7) Each bar represents a significant digit, with the least significant digit on the right.	*Depth-Attributive*

Figure 4.2: The modified Constituency Schema

58

Although the process trace will be described in terms of TAILOR's domain, the domain of complex devices, it should be possible to use it in any domain where processes occur and must be explained. The following section describes the assumptions made of a knowledge base in designing the process trace.

4.3   Requirements of the knowledge base

The process trace is dependent on the knowledge base *only* to the extent that it needs information about objects and processes. A knowledge base with information about processes presumably describes the *events*, or actions, that occur. In TAILOR, these are the events that occur when an object performs its function. The knowledge base also most probably contains information about relationships among events, such as causal or temporal relationships. A process description is represented by relationships among various events in the knowledge base. To use the process trace on an arbitrary knowledge base, one needs to be able to identify these relationships. There are three constraints:

- It must be possible to retrieve information about the events contained in the knowledge base and to identify the relationships among various events.

- If the knowledge base contains many such relationships, the relation types need to be ranked to enable the program to decide which relations to include in the text. This ranking must be done before using the process trace.

- The beginning and end of a process explanation have to be identifiable. This constraint will become clearer when the process trace is described.

To summarize, if information about events, their relationships and the start and goal states is available, the process trace can be used to produce a process explanation.

Given knowledge bases other than TAILOR's with different types of links and different representations, the implementation of the strategy (the functions which retrieve the information from the knowledge) would have to be adjusted to reflect the changes, but the process trace would remain unchanged.

4.4   The process trace: a procedural strategy

Unlike other existing strategies (such as the constituency schema), this new strategy does not impose an abstract pattern on the underlying knowledge base, but follows it closely.[2] We termed this type of strategy a *procedural* strategy. In this sense, a

---

[2]This strategy still imposes a certain viewpoint (i.e., a causal view) on the knowledge base, by choosing specific links to traverse as opposed to others.

process trace is similar to the strategy identified in a study done by Linde and Labov (1975), wherein they asked people to describe their apartments. They discovered that people generally take a visual tour of their apartment and describe it as they go along. Linde and Labov formalized this result in a discourse strategy, which we refer to as the *apartment strategy*. The apartment strategy follows the lay-out of the apartment being described, tracing the imaginary tour the speaker is taking through the apartment. The speaker may either start by describing a main hall and then describe the rooms off that hall, or may go from one room to the next if they lead to one another. The apartment strategy, however, had not been formalized as part of a generation system to produce text.³ The apartment strategy provides a physical description and not a functional one.⁴ Furthermore, the apartment strategy results in a *complete* description of the apartments (with branching points and backtracking), in that every room is generally included, although not all with the same level of detail. The apartment strategy did not account for describing apartments that are too complex to be described in that way. In the process trace, however, not every causal link will be included. In a complex knowledge base, one can expect to have many links branching out of the main path. To keep the process explanation coherent, a process trace cannot follow every causal link in the knowledge base that may branch out of the main path. Therefore the strategy needs to dictate which side links or side chains to include in the text, which to ignore, and when to mention a link (or a series of links) it has chosen to include.

The next sections describe the different types of links that may exist, how a program can identify the main path, and various choices the process trace needs to make. The process trace was identified from the texts studied. Decisions about which link types to include and when to include them were made with the assumption that, to remain coherent, the process explanation needs to focus on the main path, that is, on the main sequence of events that take place in order for the device to perform its function. The process description found in the texts studied indeed focused on this main sequence of events. As these texts presented the main sequence of events in sequential order, that is from start to finish, the process trace will duplicate this behavior. Note that it would not be hard to change the algorithm to produce a process explanation in which the events are presented in another order, if that was desirable. For example, it might be appropriate in some situation to traverse the main path in reverse, from goal to start. (We will see in Chapter 8 how this traversal order, and in fact which type of links to follow, could be controlled depending on the situation at hand). In our domain, however, a process explanation produced that way is probably less clear than one in which the events are presented in sequential order from start to goal, however. This is illustrated by the two functional descriptions of how a door lock works, shown in Figures 4.3 and 4.4. Both descriptions follow the main path. In Figure 4.3 the main path is given from the start to the goal, while it is given beginning with the goal state in

---

³Recently, Sibun (1992) developed a program to describe apartment lay-outs. This program is not based on Linde and Labov's algorithm, but it is very similar to it. Although this system uses what Sibun calls "local decisions", these could be expressed as a *global strategy* which would then resemble the process trace as we have specified it.

⁴Note, however, that the process trace could be modified to implement the apartment strategy, by changing the specification of which links to follow.

Door Locks (Simon and Schuster, 1972)

When the key is turned, it first presses the tumbler – which is kept engaged with the bolt by the pressure of a spring – upward and thus releases the bolt. The key bit (the lateral projection at or near the end of the key) then engages with the first notch on the underside of the bolt. Further rotation of the key causes the bolt to slide until the catch of the tumbler engages with the next notch on the top of the bolt.

Figure 4.3: The process explanation follows the main path from the start state to the goal state

---

Door Locks

The catch of the tumbler engages with a notch on the top of the bolt. This occurs when the bolt slides, which is caused by further rotation of the key. The first notch of the underside of the bolt is engaged by the key bit, after the tumbler is released. This is enabled by the tumbler being pressed upward when the key is turned.

Figure 4.4: The process explanation follows the main path from the goal state to the start state

---

Figure 4.4. We believe that the explanation in the first figure is clearer, as it provides events in the order in which they occur.

The texts studied did not often include other links (or chains) unless they were enabling conditions for events on the main path. We took these observations into consideration when formalizing the process trace. The various decisions that are presented in the next sections were thus based primarily on the texts examined but also on intuition about what makes a text coherent, as well as experimentation with TAILOR.

4.4.1 Identifying the main path and different kinds of links

Process information consists of links between events in the knowledge base that express different relations between events. The knowledge base created by RESEARCHER contains three types of relations among events, and therefore three types of links. These links seem typical of a knowledge base. They are:

- *Control* links: these links indicate causal relations between events, such as *cause-effect, enablement*, (which are termed here *positive* control links), as in "X causes Y" or "X enables Y", or *interruptions*, (which are called a *negative* control links), such as "X interrupts Y," .

- *Temporal* links: these links indicate temporal relations between events, such as "X happens *at the same time* as Y."

- *Analogical* links, or *correspondence links*: these indicate analogies and comparison between events, such as "X is *equivalent to* Y," or "X *corresponds to* Y."

Because these links represent relations between events, they could all be potentially mentioned in the process description. As they are potentially too numerous, there is a need to choose those that will produce a coherent process explanation. Because they express different kinds of relations, it is possible to rank them in order of importance. This ranking must be done in order for the strategy to decide which links to include in producing a process explanation, when it has to choose among several.

While the ranking does not need to be a strict ranking, if all types are equally important and can all be included in the text, the program will have to simply pick one arbitrarily. A strict ranking thus helps the decision process as it allows a program to choose the "most important" link first.

Based on texts, the ranking was determined to be as follows in the domain of devices:

1. *Control links*: as these links represent causality between events, they are the most important links for describing a process. Among those, the causal links are the most significant, as they represent the strongest positive control relationships among events: to describe the main sequence of events that take place when an object performs its function, a causal relationship is better than a mere enablement relation. In the texts studied, causal links were indeed emphasized.

2. *Temporal links*: when no control relation among events can be found, the temporal relations among events become the next most important links for producing an explanation of a chain of events in sequential order.

3. *Analogical links*, or *correspondence links*: when no control or temporal relation exist among events, analogical relationships indicating how events compare with each other become important.

4.4.2   The main path

The *main path* is the main chain of events that occur from the start to the goal. In TAILOR's knowledge base, the main path describes the sequence of events that are performed when an object achieves its function. This sequence is assumed to be linear. If another series of events happens simultaneously, it will be considered as a side chain.

Consider, for example, the subset of TAILOR's knowledge base representing the *loudspeaker* shown in Figure 4.5.[5] To simplify the figure, not all the relations have been included. In this figure and the other figures in this chapter, each labeled box represents a frame containing information about an object. For clarity, only the labeled boxes

---

[5]The knowledge base used in TAILOR is represented using a frame-based knowledge representation, where items and relations are frames with standard slots. The representation details will be shown in Chapter 6.

are shown here, instead of all the information contained in a frame. The boxes are connected with non-directed arcs that represent a parts hierarchy. So, for example, the "loudspeaker" is shown to have the following parts: an "armature," a "magnet," an "air gap" and a "diaphragm."

In the figures, *events* and *structural relations* among the objects are represented by directed arcs between objects. The "poles attract the magnet" is an example of an event. The "coil" being "wound around" the "magnet" is an example of a structural relation between two objects. Links between events are shown separately to simplify the figure, and events on the main path, that is the main sequence of events that occur when the object (the loudspeaker) performs its function, are indicated with an asterisk (*) in the figure. For this object, the main path is:

- The varying current causes the field of the electromagnet to vary;

- The varying field causes the diaphragm to vibrate;

- The diaphragm vibrating causes soundwave intensity to vary.

In this case, all the links on the main path are *control* links. There is also a side link, the *analogical* link "corresponds to."

Some of the events in the figure can be broken up into substeps (e.g., "varies" can be decomposed into "increases" and "decreases"). These substeps are also indicated in the figure. They represent the sequence of events that occur when an event is decomposed into its substeps.

Since the program needs to identify the main path before starting generation, TAILOR includes an algorithm for obtaining it. This algorithm is essentially a depth-first search with ordered backtracking. It can be summarized as follows:

- Fetch the start and goal states. In TAILOR, these are obtained from the object frame. In RESEARCHER's representation, the *function* of a device is seen as an *action* performed on an *input* to produce an *output*. The function (or purpose) of a device is represented by a relation between two entities or possibly two other events (Baker and Danyluk, 1986). For example, the function of the loudspeaker is to "change current into soundwaves." This is represented by the relation corresponding to "change," relating two entities: "current," the input, and "soundwaves," the output. The relation corresponding to the device's function and the input and output objects can be retrieved from a device's frame. The corresponding goal and start states can be obtained from examining the events these objects are involved in.

- Search starting from the goal state:

  - Take all the links in which the goal event participates. If the link is a causal or temporal one, consider the links in which the goal event is the "caused" state or the state which happens last.

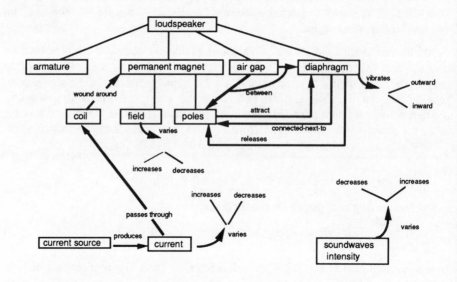

Relations (functional and physical)
Indicates that the relation has substeps
Links in the parts hierarchy

Links between events:

[current varies]*	causes	[field varies]
[current increases]	causes	[field increases]
[current decreases]	causes	[field decreases]
[field varies]*	causes	[diaphragm vibrates]
[field increases]	causes	[poles attract diaphragm]
[poles attract diaphragm]	causes	[diaphragm moves inward]
[field decreases]	causes	[poles release diaphragm]
[poles release diaphragm]	causes	[diaphragm moves outward]
[diaphragm vibrates]*	causes	[soundwave intensity varies]
[diaphragm moves inward]	causes	[soundwave intensity decreases]
[diaphragm moves outward]	causes	[soundwave intensity increases]
[diaphragm vibrates]	causes	[soundwave intensity varies]
[soundwave intensity varies]	corresponds-to	[current varies]

(Events marked with an asterisk (*) are on the main path)

Figure 4.5: Subset of the knowledge base for the loudspeaker

- Take the most important of these links (given the ranking introduced in Section 4.4.1). If several links have equal ranking, one is chosen at random. Given the chosen link, the search is repeated. The goal state is now the second event involving the chosen link. When the original start state is reached, the process stops. If the most important link does not lead to the start state, the program backtracks and starts over with the next most important link.

While searching to obtain the main path, the program also keeps track of all the other links it encounters (i.e., it tags them). After the main path has been identified, the program traverses each marked link to check both whether it leads to a side chain and whether its side chain is re-attached to the main path. This will be important in deciding whether to include the side chain or not.

As mentioned in Section 4.3, the start and goal states of a process explanation have to be identifiable to use the process trace on an arbitrary knowledge base. Without a goal state, the program would be unable to search for the main path, as there would be no beginning point for the search. Without the start state, the search for the main path would end only if there are no further relationships between the event reached and other events. A threshold could be added to ensure a halt to the search, but, at this point, no mechanism is provided to infer when the best time to stop would be. While this is the main limitation of the process trace, it is not unreasonable to assume that there would be a beginning and an end to a process explanation, whether given or inferred.

4.4.3   Deciding among several side links or side chains

In general, to produce a coherent text, one should avoid continual side-tracking on different subjects. For the process trace, this means staying roughly on the main path, without continuously following side links or side chains. In other words, the focus of the process description should be on the main path. We have determined from texts, however, that including a side link or a side chain is sometimes useful or necessary as in the following situations:

- The side link/chain introduces an analogy that provides a clearer process explanation. This was done in the junior encyclopedias texts presented earlier, and another example is shown in Figure 4.6.

- The side link/chain introduces an important side effect that the user should know about. This can happen in a medical domain, for example, when the side effect of a drug that is prescribed is of vital importance.

Side links/chains can have various structures with respect to the main path. Based on their structure and type, we classified the different overall structure of side links/chains that were encountered in the knowledge base into five cases, each of which requires different treatment:

65

Short descriptions of the loudspeaker

Consider the subset of the knowledge base given in Figure 4.5. The following description simply traces through the main path, that is the main sequence of events that take place when the loudspeaker changes current into soundwaves. Because it is a short description, no substeps are given. In this case, TAILOR was set to exclude side links.

TAILOR Output:

> The variation of the current causes the field of the magnet to vary. This causes the diaphragm to vibrate. The vibration of the diaphragm causes the intensity of the soundwaves to vary.

This second description is still a short description of the loudspeaker. This time, however, the side link "corresponds to" is included. This side link was included in the texts from the junior encyclopedia. Including this side link produces a clearer explanation of the process, as it provides a link ("corresponds-to") between the input ("the current") and the output ("the soundwave intensity"). The side link is shown in italics in the text:

TAILOR Output:

> The variation of the current causes the field of the magnet to vary. This causes the diaphragm of the loudspeaker to vibrate. The vibration of the diaphragm causes the intensity of the soundwaves to vary. *The intensity varies, like the current varies.*

Figure 4.6: An analogical side link can produce a clearer explanation

---

Diagram 1-a

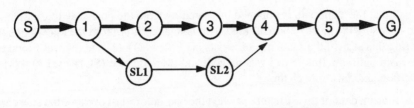

Diagram 1-b

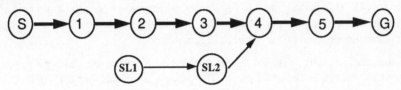

Figure 4.7: The side chain is *related* to the main path

- there is a side chain (that is a series of events) whose last event is *on* the main path. We'll refer to this situation as a side chain that is *related* to the main path;

- there is a single side link;

- there are many side links (not as part of a side chain);

- there is a side chain whose last event is *not* on the main path. We'll refer to this situation as a side chain that is *not related* to the main path;

- there are substeps.

The cases and their associated algorithms are presented below.

The side chain is related (i.e., attached at its last event) to the main path

In this case, there is a series of events whose last event is on the main path. This case can be characterized by the diagrams (1-a) and (1-b) in Figure 4.7.

In both diagrams, the main path is represented by the thick line, while the side chain is drawn as a thin line. The nodes (i.e., the circles) represent the specific events along the chain. In the diagrams, the main path from S (the start) to G (the goal) is composed of the events (S), (1) through (5), and (G). In (1-a), there is a side chain coming off the main path at (1): (1), (SL1), (SL2), (4). This side chain gets re-attached to the main path at event (4). In (1-b), the side chain does not start from an event on the main path, but gets attached to the main path at (4).

Recall that the main path is obtained by searching from the goal state to the start state and choosing the most important links available at each point in the knowledge base. During this search, the sequence of events (1) - (2) - (3) - (4) and (5) was found to be the main path, the link (SL2) was tagged, and the sequence (SL1) - (SL2) - (4) was determined to be a side chain.

A significant case of this structure is when the one-before-last event of the side chain – i.e., (SL2) – is an *enabling* condition to the last event, that is the event on the main path: this would be the case for example if (SL2) in Figure 4.7 was an enabling condition for event (4). This is illustrated in Figure 4.9, which shows both the main path for the dialing mechanism and a side chain. The (simplified) portion of the knowledge base for the dialing mechanism is shown in Figure 4.8.

If a side chain results in an event that enables an event on the main path, that side chain is mentioned in the description. The process trace specifies tracing through the side chain first, to provide the enabling condition before actually giving the causal link. After the chain is traversed, the program reverts to tracing the main path. The description of the dialing mechanism shown in Figure 4.8 is given in Figure 4.10.

There is a single side link

There are again two possibilities in this case. Each will be examined in turn. In the first case, the diagram is as shown in the first part of Figure 4.11.

Given such a single side link in the knowledge base, the decision whether to include it is based on the link type. If the link is an important link to mention as part of a description, it is included in the process trace.

In TAILOR's domain, the only links which fit this description are analogical links, as they provide a clearer explanation of the process, as previously observed. This case was illustrated in Figure 4.6. Indeed, a side link that represents a causal relationship that is not useful to the goal does not help understand a process explanation, as illustrated in Figure 4.12, where, the explanation of how a car engine turns when the ignition switch is turned is given. The causal side links are indicated in italics in the figure. Including these causal side links might hinder the readers' ability to understand the explanation as additional irrelevant information is included. This would also violate Grice's Maxims of Cooperative Behavior (Grice 1969; 1975).

On the other hand, a side link that represents an analogical link might allow readers to associate the current process explanation with an already known one and thus help them understand the process explanation. In other domains, links indicating side effects might be important and would be included. If the link is not an important link to mention, the program continues to follow the main path.

In the second case of this link structure, the diagram is as shown in the second part of Figure 4.11. If event (SL) is the cause or an enabling condition for (2), it needs to be

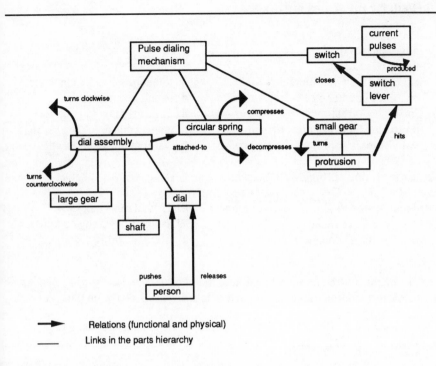

Relations (functional and physical)
Links in the parts hierarchy

<u>Links between events:</u>

[finger pushes dial]*	enables	[finger releases dial]
[finger pushes dial]	causes	[dial turns clockwise]
[dial turns clockwise]	enables	[dial turns counterclockwise]
[dial turns clockwise]	enables	[spring compresses]
[circular spring compresses]	enables	[circular spring decompresses]
[finger releases dial]*	causes	[circular spring decompresses]
[circular spring decompresses]*	causes	[dial turns counterclockwise]
[dial turns counter clockwise]*	causes	[small gear turns]
[small gear turns]*	causes	[protrusion hits switch-lever]
[protrusion hits switch-lever]*	causes	[switch closes]
[switch closes]*	causes	[current pulse produced]*

(Events marked with an asterisk (*) are on the main path)

Figure 4.8: Portion of the knowledge base for the dialing mechanism

69

Main Path for the dialing mechanism:

S:	[finger pushes dial]	enables	1:	[finger releases dial]	
1:	[finger releases dial]	causes	2:	[circular spring decompresses]	
2:	[circular spring decompresses]	causes	3:	[dial turns counter clockwise]	
3:	[dial turns counter clockwise]	causes	4:	[small gear turns]	
4:	[small gear turns]	causes	5:	[protrusion hits switch-lever]	
5:	[protrusion hits switch-lever]	causes	6:	[switch closes]	
6:	[switch closes]	causes	G:	[current pulse produced]	

Side chain coming off [*finger pushes dial*]:

S:	[finger pushes dial]	causes	SL1:	[dial turns clockwise]
SL1:	[dial turns clockwise]	causes	SL2:	[circular spring compresses]
SL2:	[circular spring compresses]	enables	2:	[circular spring decompresses]

The side chain is related to the main path, as the event *the circular spring compresses* is an *enabling* condition for the event *circular spring decompresses* in the main path.

Figure 4.9: The side chain is related to the main path: an example

---

mentioned. The strategy dictates to mention it immediately after mentioning event (2), as in the previous case. An example of this case is presented in Figure 4.13, where the side link is shown in italics.

There are many short side links

However, instead of having only one single side link as in the previous case, there are now many short links. This case can represented with the diagrams shown in Figure 4.14.

In each case (diagram 3-a, 3-b, or a combination of both), all these short side links cannot be included as the main path would be lost among the side links, resulting in a less clear description. As a result, if the links are judged to be important to mention, they are grouped together after the main path is described, and proper re-introduction of the appropriate links is necessary. In TAILOR, a parameter defines the number of short side links required to trigger this case. We will see in Chapter 8 how this parameter might be set automatically depending on the situation at hand.

Description of the pulse dialing mechanism

Because the person dials, the dial assembly of the pulse dialer turns clockwise. The dial assembly turning clockwise causes the spring to be compressed. The compression of the spring enables the spring to be decompressed.

Side-chain
(S - SL1 - SL2)
Point at which it is re-attached: **2**

The person dialing enables the person to release the dial. This causes the spring to be decompressed. The decompression of the spring causes the dial assembly to turn counterclockwise. This causes the gear of the pulse dialer to turn. The dial assembly turns counterclockwise proportionally to the way the gear turns. Because the gear turns, the protrusion of the gear hits the lever of the switch. This causes the lever to close the switch. Because the lever closes the switch, current pulses are produced.

Main path
(S - 1 - 2 - 3 - 4)

Analogical side-link

Main path
(4 - 5 - 6 - G)

Figure 4.10: Including a side chain whose one-before-last event is an enabling condition for an event on the main path

Diagram 2-a

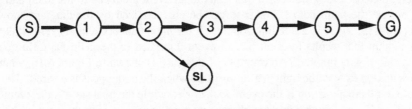

Diagram 2-b

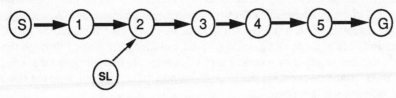

Figure 4.11: There is a single side link

71

Explaining why a car engine turns when the ignition switch is turned on

When the key is turned into the ignition switch, current flows through the starter relay coil and causes a magnetic field. This causes the starter relay contacts to close, and current to flow to the starter motor. The starter motor turns. This causes the crankshaft to turn and the engine turns over. *This causes the generator to turn.*

Figure 4.12: Including a causal side link does not render the explanation clearer

---

Description of an amplifier (generated by TAILOR)

An amplifier is a device that controls a strong current with a weak current. The variation of the weak current causes the voltage across the cathode and the grid to vary. This causes the strong current to vary. *The strong current was produced by a battery.*

Figure 4.13: Including an enabling condition

There is a side chain which is not related to the main path

Here, there is a long side chain that leads to an event unrelated to the main path, that is *not* on the main path. This case can be characterized by the diagram shown in Figure 4.15. There is a side link coming off the main path at event (1). This link leads to a chain that results in event (6), an event unrelated to the main path. In general, this side link is ignored. An example of this case is shown in Figure 4.16, where an explanation of why the light in a car turns on when the door opens is desired. The start state in this explanation is the event *door opens*, while the goal state is the event *light goes on*. To explain this process, there is no need to explain why the buzzer also goes on when the door opens. This is a side chain. It is not included in the text. In some rare cases, the side link may be essential. As mentioned earlier, this might happen in a medical domain, where side effects of drugs might be important. A side link might also be essential when it indicates a hazard, in which case it should be included as a warning. Such a side chain could then be included after tracing through the main path.[6] Another example of such a case is when there are multiple goals that need to be described. Note that event (1) has to be re-introduced before following the side chain, if the side chain is described.

---

[6]In our domain, this never happens, since, when explaining the function of a device, it is not necessary to explain all the events that also happen to take place but do not take an active part in the process sequence.

Diagram 3-a

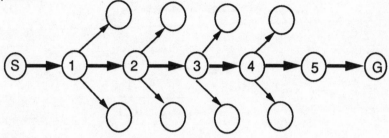

Diagram 3-b

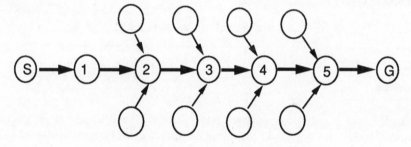

Figure 4.14: There are many short links

Diagram 4

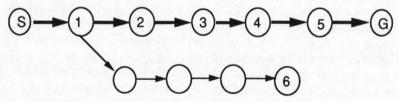

Figure 4.15: There is a long side chain which is not related to the main path

Suppose we want to describe why the light inside a car turns on when the door opens. The *start* state is the event corresponding to the *opening of the door*. The *goal* state is the *light turning on*.

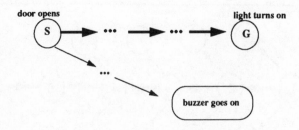

A side effect of *opening the door* also results in the *buzzer turning on*, after a sequence of other events. When explaining why the light turns on, shifting topic to describe why the buzzer turns on is unnecessary and confusing. If this side chain was judged important, it would be possible to include it by mention it at the end after proper re-introduction of the starting event.

Figure 4.16: The side chain is long and not related to the main path

Substeps

A single event might be decomposed into substeps. For example, recall the representation shown in Figure 4.5. The event *the diaphragm vibrates* consists of (1) *the diaphragm moving forward* and (2) *the diaphragm moving backward*. The causal link between the event *diaphragm vibrating* and *soundwave intensity varying* can be decomposed into two chains of events: one from *the diaphragm moving forward* and the other from *the diaphragm moving backward*. In this case, substeps are traversed if they are not too lengthy or numerous, and if they don't involve basic concepts (e.g., *electricity, voltage*) the user does not know (as indicated in the *user model*). (This is controlled by a parameter, which, in our implementation, is set arbitrarily to allow for two substeps, each having at most four links. Again, we briefly discuss in Chapter 8 how this parameter might be set automatically depending on the situation.) Including longer substep chains is undesirable for two reasons: (1) the generated text becomes too long, and (2) in the domain of complex physical devices, the process may be described at too fine a level of detail. If substeps are traced, the description explains the mechanism at the substeps level and then returns to the description at the main path level.

Substeps can also arise when a complex object is made of several other complex parts. Tracing through the main path of an object corresponds to describing how the parts achieve the object's function. It is possible to repeat the strategy for each of the subparts. This is similar to the schema recursion for the constituency schema presented in (McKeown, 1985). An example is shown in Figure 4.17.

In this description of a telephone, the process trace is first chosen to explain how the telephone transmits soundwaves in terms of the functions of its subparts, the transmitter and the receiver. The process trace then continues by explaining how the transmitter performs its function; that is, the step "changes soundwaves into current" is decomposed into its substeps.

4.5 Strategy representation

The constituency schema and the process trace are both represented in TAILOR as augmented transition networks (ATN) (Woods, 1973). The constituency schema was represented using this formalism in (McKeown, 1985), with each arc representing a rhetorical predicate. Using the same formalism for the two strategies obtains the control structure necessary to switch from one strategy to the other, thus gaining the ability to employ both strategies in the same description.[7]

The ATN corresponding to the constituency schema is shown in Figure 4.18. The arcs correspond to the predicates of the schema, thus defining the type of information to be taken from the database to include in the description. The predicates are:

- the *identification* predicate, which represents the more general concept of which the present object is an instance.

- the *attributive* predicate, which provides different attributes of an object (such as its shape or material). The attributive predicate can also functional information (such as the function of an object).

- the *constituency* predicate, which gives the components of an object, if there are any.

When several facts in the knowledge base can match the predicates or when several predicates are available, one is chosen based on factors such as *focus*, as in (McKeown, 1985). So, although the strategy imposes an abstract pattern on the knowledge base (and in that sense can be seen as imposing a global strategy), decisions as to what to include in the text also include *local decisions* at each step of the strategy (which are influenced by what is actually contained in the knowledge base and the text formed so far). This will be explained in detail in Chapter 6.

---

[7] It is important to note that we do not claim that schemas and ATNs are the best way to represent discourse strategies in general. For our task, a schema representation and its ATN implementation were elegant, convenient and efficient solutions to generate coherent multi-sentential texts. It was important to use the same formalism for both strategies, in order to be able to combine them easily. We will discuss in Chapter 8 other tasks for which these were not appropriate.

Description of an object made up of several functional complex parts

This description is generated by TAILOR to describe a telephone, when the user model indicates that the user is *naive* and more information is requested about the transmitter.

The telephone is a device that transmits soundwaves. Because a person speaks into the transmitter of the telephone, a current is produced. Then, the current flows through the line into the receiver. This causes soundwaves to be reproduced.

Process description at the top-level

More about (transmitter, receiver)? transmitter

The transmitter is a microphone with a small diaphragm. Because a person speaks into the microphone, soundwaves hit the diaphragm of the microphone. This causes the diaphragm to vibrate. When the intensity of the soundwaves increases, the diaphragm springs forward. This causes the granules of the button to be compressed. The compression of the granules causes the resistance of the granules to decrease. This causes the current to increase. Then, when the intensity decreases, the diaphragm springs backward. This causes the granules to be decompressed. The decompression of the granules causes the resistance to increase. This causes the current to decrease. The vibration of the diaphragm causes the current to vary. The current varies, like the intensity varies.

Process description for the *transmitter*
The function of the transmitter is decomposed into its substeps.

Figure 4.17: Substeps arising because of subparts

76

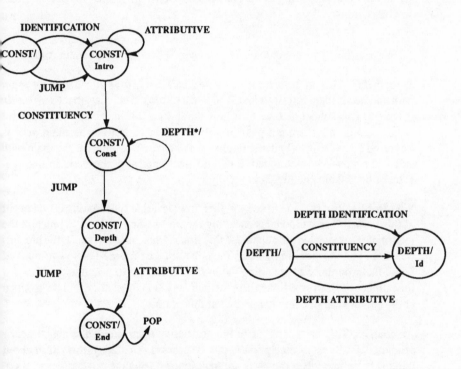

Figure 4.18: The Constituency Schema

The process of traversing the ATN for the constituency schema strategy to describe a *loudspeaker* is shown in Figure 4.19. First, the identification predicate is applied to the loudspeaker. It provides the superordinate of the object together with the function of the object. Second, the arc corresponding to the constituency predicate is taken, and the parts of the loudspeaker are retrieved, together with their properties. Finally, the depth-attributive predicate is matched against the knowledge base for each subpart.

The network for the process trace is shown in Figure 4.20. In this network, the arcs dictate how to trace the knowledge base to form a process description, mainly by following the causal links in the knowledge base. Following the process trace, the knowledge base is traversed in a specific order. These arcs are not rhetorical predicates as in the network corresponding to the constituency schema. Rather, the arcs indicate the following actions:

- *Next-main-link*: This arc dictates to follow the next link on the main path.

- *Side-chain?*: This arc tests for a long side chain that gets re-attached to the main path and needs to be followed first. If the test returns True, the subnet *side-chain* is called. This subnet dictates to follow the links of the side chain. If the chain is not coming off the main path, it will be traversed before the main path is traversed (side-chain? (1) in the figure). If the chain is coming off the main path and also needs to be mentioned, it will be mentioned after the event initiating it is mentioned (side-chain? (2) in the figure).

- *Side-link?*: A test is made to see whether there is a side link coming off an event at this point. The test includes checking the importance of the side link and the length of its associated side chain. If this link is important and short, the arc will be taken, i.e., the side link will be included. Since the side links were marked while the program was obtaining the main path, it is also possible to check for the number of short side links. If there are many side links, they will be grouped at the end instead of being mentioned at this point.

- *Attributive*: This arc is similar to the attributive predicate in the constituency schema. Hardly any description is purely process oriented; information about parts is presented when the parts are mentioned during the process description. If information about a part just introduced is available in the knowledge base, this arc will be taken.

- *Substeps?*: If an event at this point can be divided into substeps, the description does not have to be short. and the substeps do not contain basic concepts the user does not understand, each substep with its associated chain is followed. To traverse the substeps, the subnet (or subroutine) *substep* is called for each substep. This subroutine is very similar to the main graph but does not allow for a further decomposition of events.[8] If a short description is desired or if substeps include basic concepts that the user does not understand, as indicated in the user model, the program does not follow the substeps.

Stepping through the Constituency Schema to describe a loudspeaker

Applying the predicates to the loudspeaker:

Identification predicate: device
　　　　　　　　　　　(used-for: change [current] into [soundwave])

Constituency predicate: armature
　　　　　　　　　　　(shape ring, material permendur)
　　　　　　　　　　　coil
　　　　　　　　　　　magnet
　　　　　　　　　　　(mobility permanent, shape ring)
　　　　　　　　　　　diaphragm
　　　　　　　　　　　gap
　　　　　　　　　　　(shape dome, material paper, size large, thin)

Applying the depth attributive predicate to the diaphragm:
　　　　　　　　　　　(mounted-on magnet-poles)

Applying the depth attributive predicate to the gap:
　　　　　　　　　　　(contains air)
　　　　　　　　　　　(between poles magnet)

Applying the depth attributive predicate to the coil:
　　　　　　　　　　　(mounted-on magnet)

TAILOR output:

The loudspeaker is a device that changes current into soundwaves. The loudspeaker has a permendur, ring-shaped armature, a coil, a ring-shaped permanent magnet, a gap and a paper thin large dome-shaped diaphragm. The diaphragm is mounted on the poles of the magnet. The gap contains air. The gap is between the poles and the diaphragm. The coil is mounted on the magnet.

Figure 4.19: Stepping through the Constituency Schema

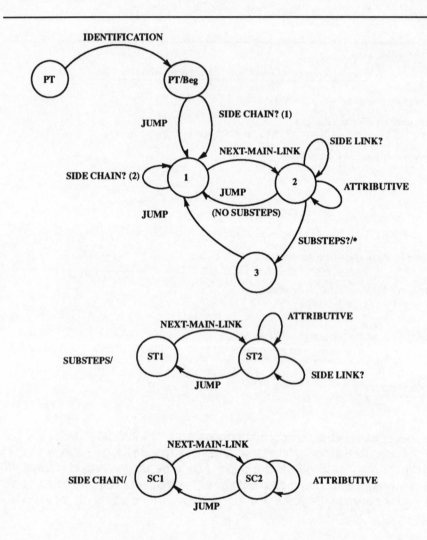

Figure 4.20: The Process Trace

Stepping through the Process trace to describe a loudspeaker

(Including substeps and a single side link)
Substeps and an important isolated side link (an analogical link)

Main Path

First Causal Link:

m-causes relates the two relations: ; The variation of the
      [current] varies   ; current causes the field
      [field] varies   ; of the magnet to vary.

Substeps: first substep: "current increases"
              second substep: "current decreases"

Causal link in the **first substep**:
    {m-causes} relates the two relations: ; When the current
        [current] increases   ; increases the field
        [field] increases   ; increases.

Next causal link in the substep chain:
    {m-causes} relates the two relations: ; Because the field
        [field] increases   ; increases the poles of
        [poles] attract   ; the magnet attract the
                [diaphragm]   ; diaphragm of the
                            ; loudspeaker.

Next causal link in the substep chain:
    {m-causes} relates the two relations: ; The poles attracting the
        [poles] attract [diaphragm]   ; diaphragm causes the
        [diaphragm] moves-forward   ; diaphragm to move
                            ; forward.

Causal link in the **second substep**:
    {m-causes} relates the two relations: ; The current decreasing
        [current] decreases   ; causes the field to
        [field] decreases   ; decrease.

Next causal link in the substep chain:
    {m-causes} relates the two relations: ; This causes the poles
        [field] decreases   ; to release the
        [poles] releases [diaphragm]   ; diaphragm.

Next causal link in the substep chain:
    {m-causes}relates the two relations: ; Because the poles
        [poles] releases [diaphragm]   ; release the diaphragm
        [diaphragm] moves-backward   ; the diaphragm
                            ; moves backward.

(Continued in the next Figure)

Figure 4.21: Process Trace for the loudspeaker

Back to the main path

Next causal link in the main path:

{m-causes}   relates the two relations: ; The variation of the
                [field] varies   ; field causes the
                [diaphragm] vibrates   ; diaphragm to vibrate.

Substeps: first substep: "diaphragm moves forward"
          second substep: "diaphragm moves backward"

Causal link in the **first substep:**
   {m-causes} relates the two relations: ; Because the diaphragm
     [diaphragm] moves-forward   ; springs forward the
     [soundwave-intensity]   ; soundwave-intensity
          decreases   ; reduces.

Causal link in the **second substep:**
   {m-causes} relates the two relations: ; The diaphragm springing
     [diaphragm] moves-backward   ; backward causes the
     [soundwave-intensity]   ; soundwave-intensity
          increases   ; to increase.

Back to the main path

Next causal link in the main path:

{m-causes}   relates the two relations: ; The variation of the
        [diaphragm] vibrates   ; diaphragm causes the
        [soundwave-intensity] varies ; soundwave-intensity to
                         ; vary

Isolated short side-link

Analogical link:
{m-corresponds-to} relates the two relations: ; The soundwave intensity
     [soundwave-intensity] varies ; varies like the current
     [current] varies   ; varies.

(English description given in the next figure.)

Figure 4.22: Process trace for the loudspeaker (Cont'd)

TAILOR output:

The variation of the current causes the field of the magnet to vary. When the current increases the field increases. Because the field increases, the poles of the magnet attract the diaphragm of the loudspeaker. The poles attracting the diaphragm causes the diaphragm to spring forward. The current decreasing causes the field to decrease. This causes the poles to release the diaphragm. Because the poles release the diaphragm, the diaphragm springs backward. *The variation of the field causes the diaphragm to vibrate.* Because the diaphragm springs forward, the soundwave-intensity of the soundwaves decreases. The diaphragm springing backward causes the soundwave-intensity to increase. *The vibration of the diaphragm causes the soundwave-intensity to vary.* The soundwave-intensity varies, like the current varies.

Figure 4.23: English output for the trace of Figures 4.21 and 4.22

The process of stepping through the ATN for the process trace strategy is shown in Figures 4.21 and 4.22, and the corresponding English is shown in Figure 4.5. In this figures, we show the process description for the loudspeaker. This description includes explaining the causal links at the substep level and includes a short side link, an analogical link. This process description is obtained by applying the process strategy to the subset of the knowledge base previously shown in Figure 4.5, page 64. The sentences that resulted from following the main path are in italics. All the links between events (e.g., m-causes) are given in curly brackets, together with the two events they relate.

The descriptions shown in this section are actually not the full descriptions TAILOR generates using the process trace strategy. Full descriptions include a statement that first introduces the object as well as attributive information about some subparts. This information is omitted here as the emphasis is on tracing links between events. Full descriptions are presented in other parts of this book.

In Figures 4.24 and 4.25, we show the process description for the dialing mechanism, which involves following a side chain. The corresponding English output from TAILOR, shown in the comments, was presented previously in Figure 4.10, page 71. The knowledge base for the dialing mechanism was shown in Figure 4.8 on page 69. In this case, it was necessary to first mention the side chain before mentioning the events on the main path, as the events on the side chain are preconditions for the events on the main path.

A text generated using the process trace follows the knowledge base very closely. The arcs of the schema do not correspond to rhetorical predicates (as they *all* correspond

---

[8] A user can explicitly ask for a further decomposition if required.

Process trace for the dialing mechanism

(including a side chain that gets re-attached to the main path)

Long side chain

First Causal Link of the side-chain:

{m-causes}   relates the two relations: ; Because a person dials, the
                [one] pushes [dial]   ; dial assembly of the pulse
                [dial-assembly] turns-clockwise   ; dialer turns clockwise.

Next Causal Link of the side-chain:

{m-causes}   relates the two relations: ; The dial assembly turning
                [dial-assembly] turns-clockwise   ; clockwise causes the
                [circular-spring] compressed   ; spring to be compressed.

Point at which the side chain is re-attached to the main path:

{m-enables} relates the two relations: ; The compression of the
                [circular-spring] compressed   ; spring enables the
                [circular-spring] decompressed   ; spring to be decompressed.

Main path

First Link:

{m-enables} relates the two relations: ; A person dialing
                [one] pushes [dial]   ; enables the person to
                [one] releases [dial]   ; release the dial.

Next Causal Link:

{m-causes}   relates the two relations: ; This causes the
                [one] releases [dial]   ; spring to be
                [circular-spring] decompresses   ; decompressed.

Next Causal Link:

{m-causes}   relates the two relations: ; The compression of the spring
                [circular-spring] decompresses   ; causes the dial assembly to
                [dial-assembly]   ; turn counterclockwise.
                        turn-counterclockwise

Next Causal Link:

{m-causes}   relates the two relations: ; This causes the gear
                [dial-assembly]   ; of the pulse dialer
                        turn-counterclockwise
                [small-gear] turns   ; to turn.

Figure 4.24: Process trace for the dialing mechanism

Analogical Link:

{m-proportional} relates the two relations: ; The dial assembly turns
       [dial-assembly]   ; counterclockwise proportion-
              turn-counterclockwise   ; ally to the way the gear turns.
       [small-gear] turns

Next Causal Link:

{m-causes}   relates the two relations: ; Because the gear turns, the
                 [small-gear] turns   ; protrusion of the gear hits
                 [protrusion] hits [switch-lever]   ; the lever of the switch.

Next Causal Link:

{m-causes}   relates the two relations: ; This causes the lever
                 [protrusion] hits [switch-lever]   ; to close the switch.
                 [switch-lever] closes

{m-causes}   relates the two relations: ; Because the lever closes
                 [switch-lever] closes   ; the switch, current
                 [current-pulse] produced   ; pulses are produced.

Figure 4.25: Process trace for the dialing mechanism – Cont'd

---

Oscillator (generated by TAILOR)

An oscillator is a device that produces a varying current when a battery produces a current. Because the battery produces a current, the transistor turns on. The transistor turning on is also caused by the capacitor discharging through the resistor. The transistor turning on causes the capacitor to charge. This causes the transistor to turn off. Because the transistor turns off, the capacitor discharges through the resistor. The resistor has low resistance. The capacitor discharging through the resistor causes the varying current to be produced.

Figure 4.26: Example of a feedback loop

---

to the *cause-effect* predicate), as they did in the constituency schema, but rather help follow the knowledge base in a coherent manner.

4.6 Open problems

In formalizing the process trace, we have assumed that the start and goal states of the sequence were known. The algorithm outlined in this section finds the main path of events by tracing the events in the knowledge base from the goal state to the start state. If no start state is provided, the search will end when the program reaches an event with no further links. If the knowledge base is very complex, this may result in a very long search. If no goal state is provided, the program cannot search for the main path and will not be able to provide a process explanation. It is unclear what strategy should be used to decide when to start and end a process description should the program have no clue as to what the start and goal states are.

The other assumption made in formalizing this strategy is that there is only one main chain of events that allow a device to perform its function. This appeared to be the case in the texts we examined. If there are several, the first one found will be chosen as the main path, and the other one will be treated as a side chain. It is unclear whether that is correct or whether there are other criteria that would allow the program to choose among several equally likely or concurrent main paths.

Lastly, while the program used to obtain the main path is able to detect loops in the main path, the resulting text at this point will not indicate that a loop was found. This can happen in case of a feedback loop. Consider for example the description of an oscillator shown in Figure 4.26. Although the program detected a loop, it is not explicitly stated in the text. Although a few changes would make the identification of loops in the generated texts possible, it is not clear what would be the best way to explain such feedback loops.

4.7 Summary

In this chapter, we have presented in detail two discourse strategies that can be used to produce descriptions of complex devices. The constituency schema is a declarative strategy identified by McKeown (1985). It consists of rhetorical predicates. Unlike other discourse strategies, the process trace is procedural in nature, in that it consists of directives for tracing the underlying knowledge base. By representing the procedural strategy in the same formalism as the declarative strategy, we are able to use the two strategies together to produce a single text. This is explained in the next chapter.

Chapter 5

Combining the strategies to describe devices for a whole range of users

In the two previous chapters, we have proposed using the constituency schema to describe an object to an expert user and the process trace for a naive user. Chapter 4 presented these strategies in detail. TAILOR can select a strategy based on the user's assumed domain knowledge level. Users are not necessarily strictly naive or expert, however, but can fall anywhere along a knowledge spectrum between the extremes of naive and expert.

In Chapter 2, we defined an expert user as one who knows many of the objects contained in the knowledge base and the basic underlying concepts necessary to understand the devices' mechanisms. A naive user, on the other hand, does not understand the basic underlying concepts and does not know about any of the objects included in the knowledge base. These two types of users clearly represent extremes. Many users are likely to fall somewhere between these extremes, as they might have some knowledge about the domain, too much to be classified as naive users but not enough to be considered experts. A generation system that can only tailor to the two extreme user types is limited and not appropriate for many users. The ability to generate descriptions aimed at users with intermediate amounts of knowledge as well as at novices and experts is required.

One way to address this problem is to define several stereotypes and categorize users in terms of these types. A discourse strategy can be assigned to each user type, and tailoring can be done based on the stereotype assigned to a particular user.

One problem with this approach is the necessity to define a set of somewhat arbitrary stereotypes, arbitrary both in terms of their number and in what they represent. Furthermore, users are forced into stereotypes, and a generation system comprising these user types can tailor its answers only to these predefined categories and is thus still limited.

In this chapter, we show how, by explicitly representing a user's domain knowledge, TAILOR is able to generate descriptions for a whole range of users rather than just an *a priori* set of user stereotypes. Based on the user model, TAILOR can merge the two strategies automatically in a systematic way to produce a wide variety of descriptions for users who fall anywhere between the two extremes of naive and expert. Therefore, TAILOR can also adapt itself to the user's continuously changing expertise.

We also show how, by representing both strategies using the same formalism (here an augmented transition network), it is possible to easily combine the strategies in many different ways. This can be generalized to any number of strategies and thus gives a generation system greater flexibility, allowing it to generate a wider variety of texts than otherwise possible.

5.1 The user model contains explicit parameters

Besides the aforementioned problems with stereotypes, it would be difficult in the domain of complex devices to categorize users in terms of several types ranging from naive to expert. Deciding on the number and type of stereotypes that might exist between the extremes would require partitioning the knowledge base into several categories and deciding that knowledge about one type of objects indicates more expertise than knowledge about another set of objects. As discussed in Chapter 2, Section 2.2, this would not be appropriate for a complex domain such as ours.

Instead of attempting to define various stereotypes for users falling inside the knowledge spectrum, we chose to explicitly represent a user's knowledge about the domain. This gives TAILOR the ability to generate descriptions to a whole range of users, ranging from naive to expert, and not just to a predefined set of user types.

In Chapter 2, we introduced the kinds of user domain knowledge that might affect the type of descriptions that can be provided in the domain of complex physical objects. They were:

- knowledge about specific items in the knowledge base. Users who fall along the knowledge spectrum may know about some items in the knowledge base and not others. We term this having *local expertise* about some objects (Paris, 1984).

- knowledge about various underlying concepts. These vary depending on the domain under consideration. In our domain, based on our text analysis, underlying concepts include *electricity* and *voltages*.

(a) The user has local expertise about the microphone and understands the basic concept of electricity:

Local expertise: *microphone*
Basic concepts: *electricity*

(b) The user is a naive user:

Local expertise: *nil*
Basic concepts: *nil*

(c) The user has local expertise about the microphone and the telephone and understands the basic concepts of electricity and magnetism:

Local expertise: *microphone, telephone*
Basic concepts: *electricity, magnetism*

Figure 5.1: Representing the user model explicitly

A user model in TAILOR contains explicit information about these two types of knowledge. It indicates the objects about which the user has local expertise, and a list of basic concepts the user understands. By using these explicit parameters to indicate the user's level of expertise, TAILOR does not require a preconceived set of user types, and there is no need to fit users into these types. The user model parameters can be set to any value, and TAILOR will generate a description accordingly.

Examples of user models are shown in Figure 5.1. In (a), the user has local expertise about the microphone and understands the concept of electricity. Lack of expertise is assumed about other objects and concepts. In (b), the user is a naive user, and the user model is empty. In (c), the user has local expertise about both the microphone and the telephone. The concepts of electricity and magnetism are also understood.

5.2   Generating a description based on the user model

Before starting to generate a text, TAILOR must decide whether to use the constituency schema or the process trace for the overall framework of the text. While constructing the description, TAILOR can switch to the other strategy, thus combining the two strategies in one text. This will be done for users with intermediate levels of expertise. There is therefore a need to specify 1) how to choose an initial strategy and 2) how to combine the strategies. In TAILOR, the decision on which strategy to use at any point is based mainly on the user model.

5.2.1 Choosing a strategy for the overall structure of the description

To choose the initial strategy, TAILOR first checks whether the frame representing the object to be described in the knowledge base contains process information. If the object has no such information in its frame, the constituency schema is chosen by default. This illustrates how the content or the knowledge base affects the choice of strategy, and, how, although the system uses a global strategy, some local decisions remain.

The object will have no information about process in its frame in two cases. First, when the object's function cannot be decomposed into a sequence of events. For example, a "cover" has no mechanism associated with it. Second, when the object's function and the way it is performed is identical to that of its superordinate in the generalization hierarchy. For example, the function of the *pulse telephone* is the same as that of a *telephone*. Process information in this case is stored in the frame of the superordinate. The *pulse telephone* frame contains the part that differs from the telephone, namely the *pulse dialer*. Although the constituency schema will be chosen for the initial strategy of the description of a pulse telephone, it will be possible to switch to the process trace to explain the function of its superordinate. Similarly, it will be possible to switch to the process trace to explain the function of the "new" (or different) part, i.e., the pulse dialer. Examples will be given shortly to illustrate this.

If there was process information (or a mechanism) associated with the object, it is possible to describe the object with either strategy. TAILOR examines the user model to check the user's local expertise and his or her knowledge of the basic underlying concepts. If the user model does not indicate any local expertise about either the object to be described or its superordinate in the generalization hierarchy, then the process trace is chosen considered. Otherwise, the constituency schema is chosen. (If local expertise is indicated about the superordinate of the object, the user will most likely be able to infer the processes for the object given his or her knowledge about the superordinate, and, therefore, the constituency schema is still adequate for the description. This is similar to the inference rules Kass (1991) suggests to build a user model.)

Once the process trace is considered, the system checks whether explaining the process would involve mentioning basic concepts the user does not understand. If this is the case, the process trace is not chosen, as it would involve steps the user is not likely to comprehend, and would result in an process explanation that will not be understandable. For example, if the process explanation of a part involves the concepts of electricity and magnetism, it will not be informative if the user does not understand them.[1] In

---

[1] This is the case only because our system does not have enough knowledge to be able to explain the basic concepts to the user. It thus reverts to a structural description.

this case, after the initial description is given, the user is given the option of obtaining a process explanation.

The constituency schema is also chosen when the user model indicates local expertise about all or most of the functionally important subparts of the object to be described.

A distinction is made between parts that play a significant role in the mechanical process of a device and other parts because knowledge about the former will help comprehend the mechanism of the device. For example, the *housing* of a telephone does not play an important role in allowing the telephone to transmit soundwaves. Knowing about the *housing* or about a *cover*, the housing superordinate in the generalization hierarchy, does not help a user understand how the telephone works. Understanding how a microphone and a loudspeaker work, on the other hand, is useful since the transmitter of a telephone is essentially a microphone, and the receiver a loudspeaker.

Functionally important parts in TAILOR are defined to be the parts that are mentioned when the object's mechanism is explained or the main parts that have a mechanism themselves. ("Main parts" denotes the first level in the parts hierarchy.) For example, the pulse dialer is a functionally important part of the pulse telephone.

If the user already knows about *most* of the functionally important subparts of a device, he or she is likely to be able to infer how the parts fit together functionally (as was pointed out in the discussion of the strategies, in Chapter 3), so it is not necessary to include a process description for the object. The overall description of a text in that case will be based on the constituency schema. "Most" is represented in TAILOR as a parameter that can be set to any value for experimental purposes.[2] If the user does not have local expertise about most of the subparts of the device, the process trace is chosen, and a process explanation of how the subparts function together is provided.

To summarize, the constituency schema is chosen as the overall structure of the text in the following cases:

1. The object has no mechanism associated with its frame in the knowledge base;

2. The user model indicates local expertise about either the object or its superordinate in the generalization hierarchy;

3. The user model indicates that the user knows about most of the functionally important parts of the object.

4. The process trace would include some basic concepts (such as voltage) the user does not understand.

The process trace is chosen as the initial strategy in all other cases.

Whether the constituency schema or the process trace is chosen as the overall strategy for the description, a mixture of structural and process information can still be provided

---

[2] Its particular value in the current implementation is half the number of functionally important parts. As for the other parameters used in TAILOR, we are now investigating how this value can be set depending on the situation.

depending on the user model. For example, if the constituency schema is chosen initially, the process trace can be used for the unknown parts, providing the user with a process explanation for these parts. Likewise, if the process trace is taken at first, structural information about the parts already known to the user is still included. "Most" only determines the initial strategy (i.e., the overall structure of the text). It does not determine whether a mixture of structural and functional information will be included.

5.2.2   Combining the strategies

To generate a description aimed at users with intermediate levels of expertise, the two strategies must be combined. Consequently, it is necessary to specify:

- *when* it is possible to switch from one strategy to the other

- *the conditions* under which it is possible to switch.

Although it would be hard without a thorough psychological study to specify exact conditions necessary for switching from one strategy to the other, we have identified heuristics that determine plausible ways to mix the strategies.

Decision points within the strategies   Whenever an object is introduced and needs to be described, the system must decide whether to provide chiefly structural or functional information. Thus, each time an object needs to be described, a strategy must be chosen, and a strategy switch might occur. This gives us some clear decision points:

- Within the constituency schema:

  - After the *identification* predicate: once the parent of an object in the generalization hierarchy (the superordinate) has been introduced, a process trace can be provided for the superordinate.

  - After the *constituency* predicate: after mentioning the parts of an object, the constituency schema dictates filling the depth identification predicate for each subpart. Instead, a functional description of one or more of the parts can be given. This was done in the *Encyclopedia of Chemical Technology* text presented in Figure 3.16 in Chapter 3, page 53, for example, where *detectors* were described with a process explanation.

- Within the process trace:

  - When a part is introduced while traversing the causal links, the process strategy dictates to include attributes of this part to describe it. Here, we could also choose to describe the part more fully with the constituency schema.

- When the subparts have to be described, the constituency schema can be used to provide structural information about them instead of including functional information.

Figures 5.2 and 5.3 summarize the two strategies with the decision points.

Switching strategy when the constituency schema is chosen initially Like the initial decision for a strategy, the decision to switch strategy is mainly based on the user model. If the initial strategy is the constituency schema, TAILOR considers switching to the process trace for the superordinate and for the subparts of the device being described. The test for switching is largely the same as the initial test. TAILOR first checks whether the object under consideration (either the superordinate or each of the subparts) has some process information in its frame, or in its superordinate's frame. If so, TAILOR examines the user model to see whether the object or its superordinate is included in the user's local expertise. Switching is considered only if it is not included.

Two more conditions are tested before switching occurs. If the process explanation of the object includes basic concepts of which the user lacks knowledge, switching does not occur. TAILOR keeps a record that switching was not allowed because of lack of knowledge about basic concepts, and, after the initial description is given, the user is given the option to ask for the process description for the part, even though it contains concepts he or she might not understand.

The last condition that needs to be satisfied before the switch can occur is a test on the length of the text constructed so far and, in case of subparts, the number of parts that need to be described using the process trace. This is done to avoid generating very long texts. A variable, which can be arbitrarily set to any value, sets a threshold beyond which the process trace will not be included at this point.[3] TAILOR remembers that the process explanations for some parts were not included because of length, and, after the text corresponding to the initial strategy is produced, TAILOR asks the user whether it should provide these explanations. When all the conditions are satisfied, TAILOR decides to switch to the process trace; otherwise, it continues with the constituency schema.

Switching strategy when the process trace is chosen initially If the process trace is chosen for the overall structure of the text, a test similar to the one described above is performed when an object has been introduced as part of the process explanation. In this case, however, switching is considered only if the user model indicates local expertise about the part just introduced. As above, a test on the length of the text generated so far and the number of parts to be described using the constituency schema is also done to determine whether the switch should occur when the part is mentioned as part of the process or, at the user's request, after the initial text is produced. Again, when all the conditions are satisfied, TAILOR switches to the constituency schema for the part.

---

[3]Note that this test can also be used to test schema recursion while going through the constituency schema, when the user model indicates local expertise about a part and switching is not allowed.

Constituency Schema (with decision points)

Identification (introduction of the superordinate)
If there is no local expertise for the superordinate
do a Process Trace for the superordinate *before proceeding*
unless this would involve basic concepts the user does not understan
Constituency (description of the subparts)
For each part, do:
If there is local expertise on this part (or its superordinate),
do **Depth-identification**
Else do a Process Trace for the part
unless it would involve basic concepts the user does not understand
Attributive

Figure 5.2: The Constituency Schema strategy and its decision points

---

Process Trace (with decision points)

Next causal link
Properties of a part mentioned during the process trace
If a fuller description of the part is desired, do
Constituency Schema for the part
Substeps
Back to next causal link

Repeat for each of the subparts:
If there is local expertise on this part (or its superordinate),
do **Constituency Schema**
Else do a Process Trace

Figure 5.3: The Process Trace strategy and its decision points

---

5.3 Examples of texts combining the two strategies

In this section, we present a number of examples of texts that demonstrate that the ability to combine the strategies based on the user model allows TAILOR to generate a wide variety of texts tailored to users along the knowledge spectrum.

The first three texts are based on the telephone. This part of the knowledge base is shown in Figure 5.4. It has been greatly simplified to include only the generalization hierarchies and the main parts of the telephone. The generalization hierarchies are indicated in thick broken lines. The other lines represent *parts-of* relationships. The mechanism of objects that have process information in their frame is summarized in the labeled box in angle brackets "[ ]." For example, the telephone has process information that allows it to "transmit soundwaves."

As shown in the figure, the *telephone* has two functionally important parts: the transmitter and the receiver. The microphone is the transmitter's superordinate in the generalization tree, while the loudspeaker is the receiver's superordinate. Also indicated in the figure, the *pulse telephone* is an instance of a telephone, with a special part, the pulse dialer.

Figure 5.5 presents a description of the telephone. The next two figures provide descriptions of the pulse telephone. In these figures, the process trace is shown in italics, and the right hand column indicates the structure of the text and when switching occurs.

In Figure 5.5, the user model indicates local expertise about the *loudspeaker*. As *most* of the functionally important parts are known to the user,[4] TAILOR initially chooses the constituency schema. As a result, the overall structure of the text is a description organized around the subparts of the telephone and their attributes.

The *telephone* is first identified with its purpose, and its subparts are introduced. Then, the constituency schema directs TAILOR to provide attributive information about each of the subparts. At this point, it is also possible to switch to the process trace for some subparts. TAILOR examines each subpart to decide whether there is a need to switch strategy for any of them. Two of the subparts have a mechanism associated with them (or with their parent in the generalization hierarchy): the transmitter and the receiver. It is thus possible to describe either of these parts with the process trace. As no local expertise about the transmitter or the microphone is indicated in the user model, TAILOR chooses to provide process information for the transmitter, switching momentarily to the process trace. Because the user model indicates local expertise about the *loudspeaker*, the receiver's superordinate, TAILOR decides to use attributive information and not a process explanation to describe this part. After the process explanation for the transmitter is completed, TAILOR returns to the constituency schema, and attributive information is provided about each of the other subparts.

---

[4]*Most* is set to *one half* of the functionally important parts in these examples.

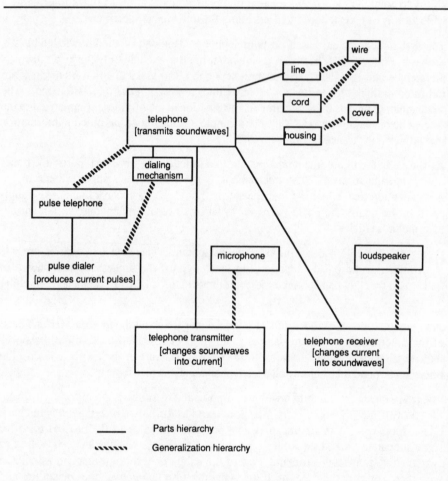

Figure 5.4: Simplified portion of the knowledge base for the telephone

---

Telephone

<u>User Model:</u>Local Expertise – *loudspeaker*
Basic Concepts – *electricity*

The telephone has two main functional parts: the transmitter (an instance of a microphone) and a receiver (an instance of a loudspeaker). Because the users knows one of the two parts of the telephone, the system decides on the *constituency schema strategy* at first. However, before providing structural information about each subpart, the system consults the user model and decides to switch strategy to describe the process of the transmitter since the user has no local expertise about it.

TAILOR Output:

The telephone is a device that transmits soundwaves. The telephone has a housing that has various shapes and various colors, a transmitter that changes soundwaves into current, a curly-shaped cord, a line, a receiver to change current into soundwaves and a dialing-mechanism. *The transmitter is a microphone with a small diaphragm. A person speaking into the microphone causes the soundwaves to hit the diaphragm of the microphone. The soundwaves hitting the diaphragm causes the diaphragm to vibrate. The vibration of the diaphragm causes the current to vary. The vibration of the diaphragm causes the current to vary.* The receiver is a loudspeaker with a small aluminum diaphragm. The housing contains the transmitter and it contains the receiver. The housing is connected to the dialing-mechanism by the cord. The line connects the dialing-mechanism to the wall.	Identification Constituency Switch to process trace for the transmitter Attributive information for the other subparts

Figure 5.5: Combining the strategies: using the constituency schema as the overall structure of the text and switching to the process trace for one part

---

Telephone with a pulse dialer

User Model: Local Expertise – *telephone*
Basic concepts – *electricity*

The *constituency schema* is chosen at first as no process mechanism is associated with the pulse telephone. When the superordinate (the telephone) is introduced, switching does not occur because the user model indicates local expertise about it. The pulse telephone has one part that the telephone does not have, that is the pulse dialer. As this part is new and no local expertise is indicated in the user model about it, TAILOR switches to the *process trace* to describe this part.

TAILOR Output:

The pulse-telephone is a telephone with a pulse-dialer.	Identification
The pulse-telephone has a pulse-dialer to produce current-pulses, when a person dials, a housing that has various shapes and various colors, a receiver to change current into soundwaves, a curly-shaped cord, a line and a transmitter that changes soundwaves into current.	Constituency
The pulse-dialer is a dialing-mechanism. A person dialing causes the dial-assembly to turn clockwise. The dial is round. The dial assembly turning clockwise causes the spring to compress. The spring is circular. A person dialing enables the person to release the dial. This causes the spring to decompress. The decompression of the spring causes the dial to turn counterclockwise. This causes a gear to turn. The gear is small. The gear turning causes the protrusion of the gear to hit a lever of the switch. This causes the switch to close. This causes current-pulses to be produced.	Switching to the process trace for the pulse dialer (includes the use of attributive predicate)
The transmitter is a microphone with a small diaphragm. The receiver is a loudspeaker with a thin small metal disc-shaped diaphragm. A dialing-mechanism is connected to a wall by the line. The housing is connected to the dialing-mechanism by the cord. The housing contains the transmitter and it contains the receiver.	Attributive information for the other parts

Figure 5.6: Starting with the constituency schema and switching to the process trace for the new part

The next two texts are descriptions of a pulse telephone, given different user models. In the first text, Figure 5.6, the user model indicates local expertise about telephones. The pulse telephone does not have a mechanism associated with its frame, as the process mechanism is associated with the telephone, its parent in the generalization tree. As a result, the constituency schema is chosen for the overall structure of the text. The pulse telephone is first introduced in terms of its superordinate, the telephone. At this point, TAILOR has the option of switching to the process trace to describe the telephone, but, as the user model indicates expertise about this object, the program does not do so. Instead, the description continues with the constituency schema. The subparts of the pulse telephone are provided. Now, TAILOR has the option of switching strategies for each subpart. Because local expertise was indicated about the *telephone*, TAILOR assumes the user also has knowledge about the telephone's parts, the transmitter and the receiver.[5] The pulse telephone has a part that the telephone does not have, however, namely the pulse dialer, an instance of a *dialing mechanism*. No expertise is indicated in the user model about this part, and TAILOR switches to the process trace to describe it. Attributive information is provided for the other parts.

In Figure 5.7, the user model shows local expertise about the *pulse dialer*. As in the previous description, the constituency schema is chosen by default for the overall structure of the description, as there is no process explanation associated with the pulse telephone.

The description thus starts by introducing the object's superordinate, as in Figure 5.6. Switching is now considered to describe the telephone. Unlike in Figure 5.6, no local expertise about the telephone is indicated in the user model. Therefore TAILOR switches to the process trace to describe it. After the telephone's mechanism has been presented, TAILOR returns to the constituency schema, and the subparts of the pulse telephone are introduced. Now TAILOR has the options of describing both the telephone transmitter and the telephone receiver using the process trace. As the text constructed so far is longer than the threshold allowed and there are two parts to describe, however, TAILOR chooses to continue with the constituency schema. Since a long description was explicitly requested, TAILOR describes these two subparts with the process trace afterwards. Because of the length of the text, substeps are preempted when going through the process trace for the parts.

Another text, shown in Figure 5.8, describes a radio station. In this example, the process trace is chosen for the initial description of the object, and switching to the constituency schema occurs for one of the parts. The user model indicates local expertise about radio transmitters. The process trace is chosen for the overall structure of the text, because the user does not know most of the parts of the radio station. The description starts by introducing the object with its purpose and following the main sequence of events that occur when the object performs its function. When the radio transmitter is introduced as part of the process explanation, TAILOR switches to the constituency schema to describe it, as the user model shows local expertise about radio transmitters.

---

[5]This is one of the inference rules employed to obtain information about the user's domain knowledge, as described in Section 2.3, page 21.

Telephone with a pulse dialer; long description requested

User Model: Local Expertise – *pulse dialer*
                       Basic concepts – *electricity*

TAILOR Output:

The pulse-telephone is a telephone with a pulse-dialer.	Identification
The telephone is a device that transmits soundwaves. Because a person speaks into the transmitter of the telephone, a varying current is produced. Then, the varying current flows through the line into the receiver. This causes the soundwaves to be reproduced.	Switch to process trace for the telephone
The pulse-telephone has a pulse-dialer that produces current pulses when a person dials, a housing that has various shapes and various colors, a receiver to change current into soundwaves, a curly-shaped cord, a line and a transmitter that changes soundwaves into current.	Constituency
The receiver is a loudspeaker with a thin small metal disc-shaped diaphragm. A dialing-mechanism is connected to a wall by the line. The housing is connected to the dialing-mechanism by the cord. The housing contains the transmitter and it contains the receiver. The transmitter is a microphone with a small diaphragm.	Attributive information for the parts
The receiver is a device that changes a varying current into soundwaves. The variation of the varying current causes the field of the magnet to vary. The magnet is permanent and ring-shaped. The field is magnetic. The variation of the field causes the diaphragm to vibrate. The vibration of the diaphragm causes the soundwave intensity to vary. The current varies like the soundwaves intensity varies.	Process trace for the receiver
The transmitter is a device that changes soundwaves into a varying current. Because a person speaks into the transmitter, soundwaves hit the diaphragm of the transmitter. This causes the diaphragm to vibrate. The vibration of the diaphragm causes the current to vary. The current varies like, the soundwave intensity varies.	Process trace for the transmitter

Figure 5.7: Switching to the process trace for the superordinate and two parts

---

100

Radio Station

User Model: Local Expertise – *radio transmitter*
              Basic concepts – *electricity*

A radio station has a few functionally important parts, only one of which is known to the user. The *process trace* is thus chosen as the overall structure of the text. TAILOR switches to the *constituency schema* for the radio transmitter as the user model indicates local expertise about it.

TAILOR Output:

A radio-station is a device that broadcasts a signal when a human speaks into a microphone. Because the human speaks into the microphone, a current is produced. Then, the current flows through the wire into the radio-transmitter. The radio-transmitter has an oscillator that produces a varying current when a battery produces another current, an amplifier that produces a strong varying audio-frequency signal from a varying audio-frequency signal, a mixer, and an amplifier to produce a strong radio-frequency signal from a radio-frequency signal. An amplifier has a vacuum-tube to produce a strong current from a power source and a metal grid. The oscillator has a high-resistance resistor, a battery, a capacitor, a low-resistance resistor and a transistor. *The current flowing through the wire into the radio-transmitter causes the strong varying radio-frequency signal to be produced. Then, the strong varying radio-frequency signal flows into the antenna of the radio-station. The antenna is long and made of metal. Because the strong radio-frequency signal flows into the antenna, the strong radio-frequency signal is broadcasted.*

Process Trace

Switch to constituency schema for the radio transmitter

Continue the process trace

Figure 5.8: Starting with the process trace and switching to the constituency schema for one part

After the radio transmitter is described with its subparts, the process explanation is resumed.

Finally, in the last text shown in Figure 5.9, the same user model as in Figure 5.5 is used for a description of the same object, the telephone, but the value of *most* was changed from Figure 5.5. *Most* now requires *more than half* of the functionally important parts to be known to the user for the constituency schema to be chosen. In Figure 5.9, the description starts with the process trace and switches to the constituency schema for the loudspeaker. In this text, a process mechanism is provided for the telephone, explaining how its main parts work together to allow the telephone to transmit soundwaves. As the user is already familiar with the loudspeaker, a fuller structural description is provided for the receiver, an instance of a loudspeaker. This text would be appropriate for a user who would not be able to infer how the telephone functioned knowing only how the loudspeaker functions.

Compare this text with the one in Figure 5.5, repeated in Figure 5.10 for ease of comparison. In this text, only a structural description is provided for the telephone. A process explanation is provided for the transmitter, however, because this part is unknown to the user. This text would be appropriate when the user is able to infer how the telephone's mechanism, knowing how the receiver works and given the process explanation for the transmitter. It is unclear which of these texts is "best" for a user who has local expertise about loudspeakers. This is an indication that testing is needed to set the value of *most*. It is likely, however, that no unique value actually exists: it might depend on the kind of object being described, the user's learning style, and other factors.

In either case the mixture of functional and structural information seems appropriate given the user's domain knowledge. These two texts are included to illustrate how, although *most* chooses the overall structure of the description, a mixture of process and structural information is still provided.

The texts presented in this section seem to be appropriate for the users they are tailored to as they provide functional details when the user lacks such information and structural details when the user probably already has the functional understanding of the object. The heuristics provided here allow the system to generate reasonable descriptions given the user's domain knowledge. Note, however, that as is generally the case in text generation, there are no clear "best" texts, and extensive testing would be required to determine the descriptions effectiveness.

5.4 Combining strategies yields a greater variety of texts

Independent of whether the texts provided here are the most appropriate for a given user, the ability to combine strategies is important, because it allows TAILOR to generate a greater variety of texts than would otherwise be possible. For example, for the pulse

---

Telephone

<u>User Model</u>:   Local Expertise – *loudspeaker*

                   Basic concepts – *nil*

The value of *Most* was changed to require more than one half of the functionally important subparts to be known to the user before the constituency schema could be chosen. As a result, the process trace was chosen here. The constituency schema is used to describe the receiver because the user model indicates local expertise about the loudspeaker.

TAILOR Output:

The telephone is a device that transmits soundwaves. Because a person speaks into the transmitter of the telephone a varying current is produced. Then, the varying current flows through the line into the receiver. The receiver has a thin small metal disc-shaped diaphragm, a gap, a ring-shaped permanent magnet, a coil and a ring-shaped permendur armature. The diaphragm is mounted on the poles of the magnet. The gap is between the poles and the diaphragm and it contains air. The coil is wound around the magnet. *Because the varying current flows through the line into the receiver, soundwaves are reproduced.*

Process trace for the telephone

Switch to constituency schema for the loudspeaker

Process trace

More about (transmitter)?: nil

Figure 5.9: Changing the parameter that determines the overall structure of a description

---

Telephone

<u>TAILOR</u> Output:

The telephone is a device that transmits soundwaves. The telephone has a housing that has various shapes and various colors, a transmitter that changes soundwaves into current, a curly-shaped cord, a line, a receiver to change current into soundwaves and a dialing-mechanism. *The transmitter is a microphone. A person speaking into the microphone causes the soundwaves to hit the diaphragm of the microphone. The soundwaves hitting the diaphragm causes the diaphragm to vibrate. The vibration of the diaphragm causes the current to vary. The current varies, like the intensity varies.* The receiver is a loudspeaker with a small aluminum diaphragm. The housing contains the transmitter and it contains the receiver. The housing is connected to the dialing-mechanism by the cord. The line connects the dialing-mechanism to the wall.

Figure 5.10: Description of the telephone. *Most* is set to half of the functionally important parts

telephone which has a superordinate and three functionally important parts, TAILOR can generate eight different descriptions, even though the constituency schema is always chosen as the initial strategy (as the pulse telephone has no mechanism in its frame). These various descriptions are outlined below with the corresponding user model:

- The user model is nil: the process trace is chosen for the telephone and each of the parts.

- The user model indicates local expertise about the telephone: the process trace is chosen for the pulse dialer, the only part that differs from the telephone.

- The user model indicates local expertise about the receiver: the process trace is chosen for both the transmitter and pulse dialer.

- The user model indicates local expertise about the transmitter: the process trace is chosen for both the receiver and pulse dialer.

- The user model indicates local expertise about the pulse dialer: the process trace is chosen for the telephone.

- The user model indicates local expertise about the telephone and the pulse dialer: the constituency schema is chosen for the whole description.

- The user model indicates local expertise about the receiver and the pulse dialer: the process trace is chosen for the transmitter.

- The user model indicates local expertise about the transmitter and the pulse dialer: the process trace is chosen for the receiver.

Note that this number takes into account the fact that the heuristics chosen in TAILOR limit the number of combinations allowed. Furthermore, there could be yet more combinations due to the user knowing or not knowing basic concepts.

The ability to combine strategies allows a generation system to have distinct strategies clearly defined without losing flexibility. Discourse strategies help a system to construct a text with a given structure, and it is desirable to have such strategies to constrain the generation process. Given the strategies and no mechanism for combining them, a system is limited in the kinds of texts it can generate by the number of strategies. If combining strategies can be achieved, the variety of texts that can be generated is greatly increased.

Because, in TAILOR, each of the two strategies is represented by an ATN, they can be easily combined. The arcs of the ATN indicate how to go from one node to another. Jumping from a node in one network to a node in another network is as easy as going from one node to another in the same network. As a result, the control strategy needed for switching strategies is readily available with the ATN formalism and should be taken advantage of.

To combine the strategies, the potential decision points and entry points have to be decided upon. "Jump < entry-point >" arcs between the two strategies can be added at the decision points. Tests on the arcs can control the combinations. These tests can incorporate a number of factors, including the information contained in the knowledge base, the discourse produced so far, and a user model.

In the TAILOR descriptions shown so far, the decision points in the strategies and the tests combining the strategies were set to allow switching only when a new object was introduced and needed to be described. The entry points into the strategies were always at the beginning, because switching was done to describe a new object. This does not have to be the case in general. For example, consider the text in Figure 5.11 describing a telephone.

In this text, both structural and functional information are used to describe only the telephone (not its subparts). The constituency schema was chosen at first, and TAILOR jumped to the process trace after providing the parts of the telephone, to include a process trace for the telephone as well. TAILOR does not return to the constituency schema after the process trace is given, and the process trace is entered after the introductory statement, to start the process trace immediately. Similarly, in Figure 5.12, a strategy switch occurs for the same object at an entry point other than the beginning. These two texts were generated by modifying the ATN used by TAILOR to show the feasibility of mixing strategies in ways other than the ones already defined. To produce these texts, only the tests at the decision points in the strategy were changed.

Combining strategies is by no means limited to two strategies as in TAILOR. A generation system having a number of discourse strategies could combine them in a variety of

---

Telephone

TAILOR Output, using different settings:

This description starts with the constituency schema and switches to the process trace, for the telephone itself, after providing the subparts of the telephone.

The telephone is a device that transmits soundwaves.	Identification
The telephone has a housing that has various shapes and various colors, a transmitter that changes sound-waves into current, a curly-shaped cord, a line, a receiver to change current into soundwaves and a dialing_mechanism. *When a human speaks into the transmitter of the telephone, a varying current is produced. Then,*	Constituency
the varying current flows through the line into the receiver of the telephone. This causes soundwaves to be reproduced.	Switch to process trace for the telephone itself

Figure 5.11: Combining the strategies

Telephone

TAILOR Output:

This description starts with the process trace and switches to the constituency schema.

The telephone is a device that transmits soundwaves. When a human speaks into the transmitter of the telephone, a varying current is produced. Then, the varying current flows through the line into the receiver of the telephone. This causes soundwaves to be reproduced. The transmitter is a microphone with a small disc-shaped metal thin diaphragm. The line is a wire. The receiver is a loudspeaker with a small disc-shaped metal thin diaphragm.	Process trace
	Switch to constituency: Attributive information about the subparts

Figure 5.12: Combining the strategies, using an entry point other than the beginning

---

ways. Once the entry points, decision points and tests are chosen, jump arcs between the various subnets can be added. These strategies yield more flexibility and power in the kinds of texts a system can generate. (In designing the tests, however, one would have to make sure that coherence is not hindered when the system switches from one strategy to another one.)

The TEXT system was also able to combine several strategies with a recursion mechanism (McKeown, 1985). McKeown pointed out that the predicates could be expanded into schemas. As a result, instead of simply matching a predicate against the knowledge base, the corresponding schema could be traversed recursively. This was not fully implemented in TEXT, however, and the test on recursion was based only on the predicate type and the amount of information contained in the knowledge base. TAILOR is also able to use the strategies recursively, in a similar way to TEXT, except that the test for recursion also involves the user model.

Expanding on a predicate using recursion is only one of the ways to combine strategies. Combining them as explained above allows mixing strategies of different types in a variety of ways, since entry points are not necessarily limited to the beginning of the strategy and control does not have to return to the first strategy. This can only add flexibility to a generation system.

5.5 Conclusions

This chapter showed how TAILOR can automatically combine the two strategies presented earlier to provide descriptions to users with intermediate levels of expertise. By representing explicitly the user's domain knowledge in terms of parameters, TAILOR does not require an *a priori* set of stereotypes but can provide a wide variety of descriptions for a whole range of users between the extremes of naive and expert.

We showed how it is easy to combine discourse strategies when they are represented using the same formalism, here an augmented transition network.. Combining strategies gives a generation system more flexibility and allows it to widen the range of texts it can generate.

Chapter 6

TAILOR system implementation

We have implemented the discourse strategies presented in previous chapters in TAILOR, a program that generates descriptions tailored to a user's level of expertise. The discourse strategies guide the program to choose the appropriate information from the knowledge base, which is in the RESEARCHER's format. TAILOR looks at the information contained in the user model to decide on the strategy to employ. The strategy implementation as well as other components of TAILOR are discussed in this chapter.

TAILOR is implemented in Portable Standard Lisp (PSL) and runs both on an HP 9836 Workstation and an IBM 4381 under VM/CMS. The knowledge base its uses contains information about a number of complex devices such as telephones, radio transmitters and amplifiers.[1]

6.1   System overview

TAILOR is the generation component of a question-answering system for RESEARCHER, as shown in Figure 6.1.

Requests for descriptions are given in the following form:

---

[1]The information contained in the knowledge base reflects that contained in the texts read from the encyclopedias and other sources. Simplifications that have been made in the texts are thus also made in the knowledge base. This work is more concerned with retrieving information from a knowledge base than with representing physical devices in the most accurate way.

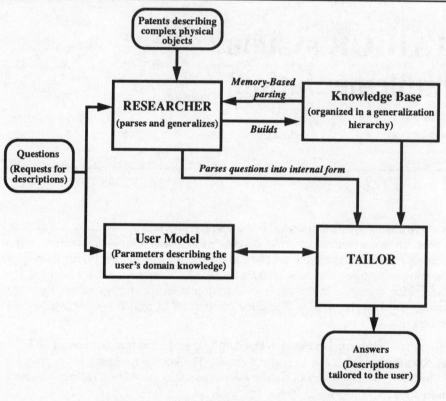

Figure 6.1: RESEARCHER and the TAILOR System

Describe X

where X is an object contained in the knowledge base. In the ideal system, RESEARCHER would parse questions using the same parser as the one it employs for parsing patent abstracts, and would then hand a representation of the question to the question-answering system. TAILOR's task is to decide how to answer the question.

A block diagram of TAILOR is shown in Figure 6.2. TAILOR is divided into two major components:[2]

1. The *textual component* determines the content and organization of the description to be generated. This is the main emphasis of the work. The textual component examines the knowledge base and chooses appropriate facts based on the level of expertise of the user and a discourse strategy. The output of this component is a conceptual representation of the content and organization of the description. The textual component is described in Section 6.4.

2. The *tactical component* takes the conceptual representation produced by the textual component and produces English. It is composed of two parts:

   - The *dictionary interface*, which takes the conceptual representation produced by the textual component and chooses the syntactic structure of each proposition. It also assigns lexical items for the various concepts contained in the description. This process is described in Section 6.5. The output of the interface is a deep structure representation of the sentences to be generated. Because the emphasis of this work has been on the textual component, the complexity and subtleties of lexical choice have not been studied in depth.

   - The *surface generator*, which takes the output of the interface and constructs English sentences. The surface generator used by TAILOR is based on the one used by the TEXT system (McKeown, 1985). The generator unifies the input with a functional grammar (Kay, 1979) to produce English sentences. The surface generator is presented in Section 6.6.

The remainder of this chapter describes the implementation of the components of TAILOR. Before describing each component of the system, the content and structure of the knowledge base are presented in Section 6.2, as both affect the kinds of descriptions that can be generated by TAILOR. Furthermore, since the user model plays an important role in TAILOR, it is discussed in Section 6.3, before the components of the system. The user model in TAILOR contains parameters representing the user's assumed domain knowledge.

---

[2]This is a simplification of the generation process, as already mentioned in Chapter 1.

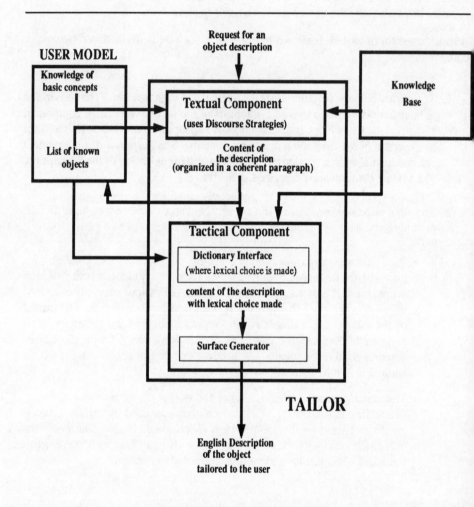

Figure 6.2: The TAILOR System

6.2 The knowledge base and its representation

Without an inference engine, any generation system is constrained by the knowledge base it uses, as it cannot include in a text information that is not explicitly contained in the knowledge base. Because the emphasis of this work was on generation, not on knowledge representation, and since knowledge representation issues had already been addressed as part of the RESEARCHER project in (Wasserman and Lebowitz, 1983; Wasserman, 1985), we decided to use the knowledge representation as previously developed. Nevertheless, as is often the case, the development of the generation system resulted in a few modifications of the knowledge base representation, mainly in the representation of process information.

The knowledge base contains detailed descriptions of complex devices organized in generalization hierarchies. The knowledge base contains about 120 object frames and 150 frames of other types. Simplified diagrams of parts of the knowledge base are shown in Figure 6.3 and 6.4. Figure 6.3 shows a subset of the parts hierarchies, while Figure 6.4 presents a subset of the generalization hierarchies.

The knowledge base include three kinds of information about the objects:

- *structural information* indicating both what the components of an object are and how objects are spatially related to each other.

- *attributive information*, that is, properties associated with the objects, such as color and shapes.

- *functional information* showing how objects achieve their function.

These three kinds of information restrict the kinds of descriptions TAILOR can generate. For example, TAILOR cannot provide a description that includes an historical development of a device, or a cost/performance evaluation, since that information is not included in the knowledge base.

The knowledge base representation employed here is a framed-based representation, where the basic frames represent entities. Entities include the physical devices that are being represented, such as "disc-drive" and "magnet" and more abstract concepts such as "current" and "side." Other types of frames are used to represent events and their relationships (such as causal relationships). Each frame type is reviewed in turn. See (Wasserman and Lebowitz, 1983; Wasserman, 1985) for more details about the representation.

The basic structure of an entity is shown in Figure 6.5. The *type* slot of the frame indicates whether the object can be decomposed in terms of other parts or is a single indivisible structure. For example, a "disc-drive" is composite, as it comprises several other parts, while a "diaphragm" is unitary.

If the object is unitary, a shape descriptor that includes properties about the object is included in the *structure* slot. If the object is composite, the frame includes a list of

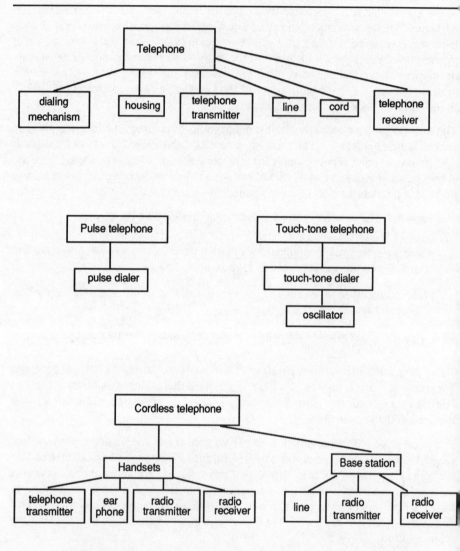

Figure 6.3: The knowledge base used in TAILOR; parts hierarchies

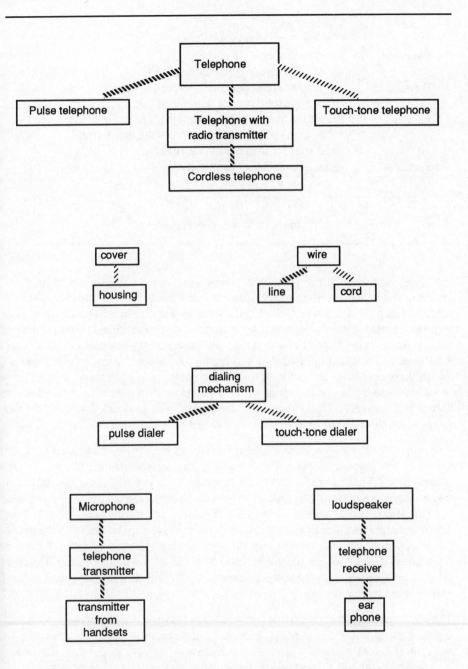

Figure 6.4: The knowledge base used in TAILOR; generalization hierarchies

Name:	name of object
Type:	"unitary" or "composite"
Structure:	a shape-descriptor if unitary;
	a list of relation records if composite.
Properties:	a list of properties and their respective values.
Components:	a list of the object parts (pointers to the frames)
Purpose:	a relation that represents the object's function in terms
	of an *input* and an *output*, representing the start and
	goal state for the process description.
Events-in:	a list of events the object participates in.

Figure 6.5: An object frame

the object subparts (a list of pointers to the subparts) in the *components* slot, and the *structure* slot includes a list of relation records that indicate how the parts are spatially related to each other. Each relation record represents a static physical relation between two objects and is also represented by a frame. A compositional primitive based scheme has been developed to support the wide variety of physical relations that exist. It is based on the five primitives shown in Figure 6.6. In most cases, however, one or two of these primitives are sufficient to describe a relation. For example, the physical relation *on-top-of* can be described with the two primitives *contact* and *location*, as shown in Figure 6.7. (A complete description of the representation scheme for the physical relations can be found in (Wasserman and Lebowitz, 1983).)

The *properties* slot of the frame contains features of the device, such as its color or material. The *purpose* slot of a device frame is used to represent the *function* of the object. This function is expressed as a relation between two entities or possibly two other relations (Baker and Danyluk, 1986). As an example, the microphone's function is to transform "soundwaves" into a "varying current," as shown in Figure 6.8. The microphone purpose slot thus contains the *relation frame* corresponding to the event *the soundwaves are transformed into current*. In the figure, this relation frame is represented with its unique identifier, &p-rel7. In all the figures included in this chapter, the English noun-phrases in brackets are provided only for clarity and do not appear in the representation.

The decision to explicitly represent a device's function as a relation between an input and an output was made partially because of the necessity to be able to retrieve the start and goal states of a device's mechanism to be able to generate a process explanation. With this representation, the goal and start state of the main sequence of events can be easily obtained. As a relation frame, in turn, contains information about causal relationships it participates in, the causal links of an object's mechanism can be retrieved through the object's purpose slot. This will be explained in more detail in

Primitive	Description	Values
distance	distance between two objects (e.g., near, remote)	0 to 10 0 - close; 10 - far
contact	strength of contact (e.g., touching, affixed)	-10 to 10 -10 - close; 10 - loose
location	relative direction between objects (e.g., above, left)	2D or 3D angle with reference frame
orientation	relative object orientation (e.g., parallel, perpendicular)	2D or 3D angle
enclosure	description of full or partial enclosure (e.g., encircled, cornered)	"full" or "partial" plus an enclosure (shape) description

Figure 6.6: Primitives used to describe static physical relations (Wasserman, 1985)

Physical relation: ON-TOP-OF

Relation name: on-top-of
Contact: unknown
Location: (side-view 90 degrees)

Figure 6.7: Example of a relation (Wasserman, 1985)

Name: microphone
Purpose: (&p-rel7 [p-transforms soundwaves → current])

Figure 6.8: Representation of a microphone's function

Category	Description
amount	amount of some entity is being changed (e.g., increase, decrease)
movement	the location of an entity is changed (e.g., pull, move)
state-change	the state of an entity is being changed (e.g., disengages)
descriptive	similar to spatial relations but involves a force (e.g., supports, holds)
domain-dependent	actions that are domain dependent, such as IO functions performed by a disc drive (e.g., read, write)

Figure 6.9: Categories of dynamic relations

Section 6.4.2.

The last slot in an object frame is the *events-in* slot. This slot indicates which actions, or events, the object participates in. For example, if the spindle of the disc-drive rotates, the event corresponding to this rotation would be included in the events-in slot of the spindle. The original representation scheme developed for RESEARCHER had concentrated on representing static spatial relations, such as *on-top-of* or *inside-of*. Because of the importance of dynamic relations (such as *rotation*) to describe the process information, the original scheme was extended to allow for dynamic relations, or events. These events were classified into the five categories shown in Figure 6.9. A set of primitive features similar to those used for spatial static relations is used to describe events in each category.

Relationships among functional events are represented by links between the event frames (or relation frames), called *event-links*. These links represent *control*, *temporal*, and *correspondence* or *analogical* relations, as discussed in Chapter 4. Control relations include: cause-effect, enablement, control, limiting, preventing, interrupting and terminating. Temporal relations indicate whether an event happens before, after, or at the same time as an another event. Correspondence relations are used when an event is proportional or equivalent to another one.

An event link is represented as a frame which contains a slot for the link type (i.e., control, temporal, or correspondence), and slots that indicate which events are related by the link. As a naming convention, these events are considered to be the *subject* and the *object* of the link. For example, that control link corresponding to "<state X> causes <state Y>" would have <state X> as its subject and <state Y> as its object. Both <state X> and <state Y> would also have a pointer back to the event-link. Thus each event frame also contains a slot that indicates the event-links in which this particular event participates. An example of this representation is shown in Figure 6.10. The top frame represents a causal link between two events. Its subject and object slots contain a pointer to the appropriate relation record. These relation records are shown underneath. Each has a slot indicating that they take a part in the causal link.

6.2.1 The generalization hierarchies

Entities in the knowledge base are organized in generalization hierarchies, thus defining prototypes: when two objects are similar, RESEARCHER extracts their identical features to form a generalization prototype (Wasserman, 1985). This allows for a more compact representation, as redundant information is stored only once. Two additional slots in an object's frame indicate whether the object is an instance of a more generic class of objects (*variant-of* slot) and whether the object itself is a generalization (*variants* slot). (These slots were not shown in Figure 6.5.)

As an example, Figure 6.11 shows the representation of the "microphone," which has a variant, namely the "telephone-transmitter," and which is a variant-of a "device." Because the microphone has subparts, its type is "composite," and its structure slot includes relation records. &reln are the unique identifiers of the relation records. For example, &rel1 in the figure indicates that "the diaphragm is clamped." &rel1 is an instance of the relation frame that corresponds to the relation "clamp." Similarly, &p-rel7 is a relation record for the dynamic relation "transform." It is used here to indicate the function of the microphone. &memn are the unique identifiers for object frames. For instance, &mem36 is the identifier of the "transmitter" frame.

Each different object can be part of a generalization hierarchy. As a result, the knowledge base contains numerous generalization trees. This is illustrated in Figure 6.12, where the main object, the telephone, is a member of one generalization tree while its subparts are members of different one. In this figure, the solid lines represent the parts hierarchies and the broken ones the generalization hierarchies.

Telephone 1 has four parts: a housing, a transmitter, a receiver, and a pulse dialing mechanism. Telephone 2 is very similar, except that its dialing mechanism is a touch-tone dialing mechanism. These two telephones are represented as instances of the prototypical frame *telephone*. This frame has four parts: a housing, a telephone transmitter, and telephone receiver, and a generalization of the dialing mechanism.

119

Link between two events:

```
name       = m-causes [control]
subject    = &rel4
object     = &rel22
rec-type   = event-link
id         = &mr2
```

         Subject Event: &rel4
```
            class           = purpose
            subject         = &mem8 (diaphragm)
            rel-frame       = p-vibrates
            event-links-in  = (&mr2)
            substeps        = (&rel6, &rel5)
                              (moves forward, backward)
```

         Object Event: &rel22
```
            class           = purpose
            subject         = &mem19 (current)
            rel-frame       = p-varies
            event-links-in  = (&mr2)
            substeps        = (&rel6, &rel5)
                              (increases, decreases)
```

Figure 6.10: Representation of events and links between events

---

Name:	microphone
Type:	composite
Structure:	(&rel1 [diaphragm clamped])
Components:	(&mem2 [resonant-system], &mem2 [diaphragm])
Purpose:	(&p-rel7 [p-transforms soundwaves → current])
Variants:	(&mem36 [telephone-transmitter])
variant-of:	(device)

Figure 6.11: Representation of a microphone

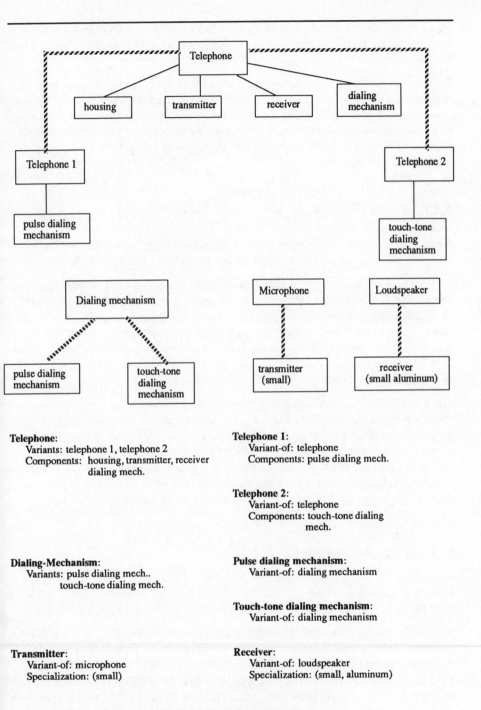

Figure 6.12: Several generalization trees

Furthermore, the transmitter and the receiver were already members of some generalization tree. Issues of creating a generalization hierarchy have been described at length in (Wasserman, 1985).

Each object frame contains information about how it differs from its parent. For example, the telephone transmitter is a microphone with a small diaphragm. The frame corresponding to the microphone contains the small diaphragm as a component, and also indicates that this part is to be substituted to the microphone's diaphragm whenever necessary. Similarly, when an object has a purpose different from its parent's, it is indicated in the object frame.

6.2.2   Limitations of the knowledge base

As pointed out at the beginning of this section, a knowledge base restricts the kinds of texts that could be generated. Two limitations are important to mention here.

There is no mechanism to explicitly represent functional comparisons and analogies. For example, it is not possible given the knowledge base and without an inference mechanism to determine the fact that a loudspeaker is a microphone in reverse. As a result, given a user model indicating expertise about microphones, TAILOR will not be able to describe the loudspeaker in terms of the microphone. Instead, TAILOR would consider the user a naive user with respect to loudspeakers, and produce the same text as if the user had no local expertise about microphones.

The other limitation is the inability to represent general laws of physics, such as *gravity* or *Newton's laws*. Therefore, TAILOR cannot describe the function of an object by simply mentioning the general law by which it can be explained. Adding the ability to represent such concepts would allow for the generation of more types of descriptions and would also add another factor to the tailoring, as it would be possible to explain a device mechanism either by explaining the sequence of events that take place (as is done in TAILOR) or by explaining the general mechanism involved.

6.3   The user model

Already presented in Chapter 2, the user model is characterized in Figure 6.13. It contains two parameters indicating whether the user has two types of knowledge.

The *local expertise* parameter indicates about which specific objects the user is knowledgeable. This parameter is represented by pointers into the knowledge base to avoid duplicating a portion of the knowledge base in the user model.[3] Knowledge about basic concepts is indicated by a list of concepts. By using this explicit representation, it is possible to set the parameters to any value for users inside the knowledge spectrum.

---

[3]This is called an *overlay* model (Carbonell, 1970; Carr and Goldstein, 1977). With this model, the user's knowledge is assumed to be some subset of the system's knowledge.

Local expertise about specific objects: *Pointers into the knowledge base*

Knowledge about basic concepts: *A list of concepts*

Figure 6.13: A characterization of the User Model in TAILOR

(a) The user has local expertise about microphones and understands two of the basic concepts:

Local expertise: &mem1 `(microphone)`
Basic concepts: `(magnetism; voltage)`

(b) The user has local expertise about telephones and radio transmitters and understands one of the basic concepts:

Local expertise: &mem46 `(telephones)`
                     &mem85 `(radio-transmitter)`
Basic concepts: `(voltage)`

(c) The user is a naive user:

Local expertise: `nil`
Basic concepts: `nil`

(d) The user is an expert user:

Local expertise: `expert`
Basic concepts: `all`

Figure 6.14: More examples of user models in TAILOR

Examples of user models are shown in Figure 6.14. (Some were already shown in Figure 5.1 in Chapter 5, page 89.)

A *naive* user is one whose user model is empty, as shown in (c) in Figure 6.14. While the stereotype *novice* can be retained as a shorthand for users falling at that extreme of the continuum, the corresponding user model can still be represented explicitly. The user model for an expert user is given in (d) in the figure, where *expert* is used instead of a huge list of objects.

Notice that the user model is coarse grained, in that it contains a list of objects the user knows and whether he or she understands the basic underlying concepts. A more detailed model might include exactly which facts the user knows about objects, and how much the user understands the basic concepts. This representation was chosen because we feel that a more detailed user model would be much harder to obtain.

6.4   The textual component

TAILOR's textual component decides on both the content and the organization of the description to be generated. Upon receiving a request for a description, TAILOR decides whether to include chiefly structural information, using the constituency schema, or functional information, using the process strategy, or a mixture of both. This decision is not based on the question type since both strategies can be used to provide an answer to a request for a description. It is instead based on the content of the knowledge base and the user's expertise level. The discourse strategies presented in earlier chapters guide the generation process by selecting information from the knowledge base. The strategies also impose order on the chosen information, thus providing the text organization.

6.4.1   Initially selecting a strategy

The first step in generating a description is to select the discourse strategy that will determine the overall content and organization of the text. TAILOR can initially choose one of two discourse strategies to provide a description. This initial choice is based on the content of the knowledge base and the user model. The decision algorithm was presented in Chapter 5 and is only summarized here, with a few supplementary implementation details.

This algorithm is shown in Figure 6.15. In the first step, TAILOR examines the knowledge base to check whether the object to be described has a mechanism associated with it, in which case TAILOR has the choice of describing the device using either strategy. This is done by checking the value of the *purpose* slot (which indicates the function) in the device's frame. If the object frame indicates a function, the decision is based on the user model as described in the previous chapter and shown in the figure.

Is there a mechanism associated with the object to be described?
  i.e., Check the purpose slot
        No: Use the constituency schema
        Yes: Is the object to be described (or its superordinate) in
                  the user model? (i.e., does the user have local expertise
                  about this object or its superordinate?)
                  Yes: Use constituency schema
                  No: Collect all the functional parts of the object.
                          If the user has local expertise about most of these
                          parts,
                              use the constituency schema
                          Else check that process information does not involve
                                basic concepts the user does not know and
                                use process trace

Figure 6.15: The decision algorithm

<control links; temporal links; correspondence links>

Figure 6.16: Importance scale used to find the main path

6.4.2 Finding the main path

The main path is used to generate a process explanation. In order to find the main path, it is important to recognize that links between events play different roles (i.e., are of different types), as, when tracing the knowledge base, the program needs to choose among several such links. One way to achieve this is to assign rankings. Then, based on this ranking, a choice can be made. There is thus a need for an importance ranking indicating for each link type its relative importance in order to produce a process explanation. The ranking used in TAILOR is shown in Figure 6.16.

This scale was selected because, based on texts, it appears that control links are the most important links to mention when providing a process explanation. If no control link can be found between two events, a temporal one is the next best choice.

We chose to represent all the rankings as parameters, as opposed to embedding the importance factors in a procedure, to be able to easily change the scales. In a domain with different scales, the parameter can be changed to reflect these differences in link importance.

Within each link type, there is also an importance factor, in order to decide among several links of the same type. In TAILOR's knowledge base, control relations are divided into two groups:

1. the *positive control relations*, which include (from highest to lowest ranking): cause-effect, enablement and control.

2. the *negative control relations*, which include limiting, preventing, interrupting and terminating.

Temporal relations are also ranked: first the precede relation, then the relation which represents same-time-as. Figure 6.17 summarizes the different link types and their respective importance rankings.

To find the main path, the program must first find the start and goal states of the main path. These are indicated in the function (purpose) slot of the object, as indicated in Section 6.2. The main path is found by searching through the links between events, going from the goal state to the start state. Starting from the goal state, the program looks at all the links linking other states to the one currently under consideration, performing an ordered depth-first search. All of these links are included in the events-in slot of the frame being considered. When there are several links to choose from, TAILOR picks one based on their importance ranking, and now considers the other event as its current state. In this manner, the program goes through the links that connect various events, until it reaches the start state, backtracking if necessary.

To choose among different links, the program checks the importance ranking of the link types according to the importance scale given in Figure 6.16. The importance scale indicates which link types are most likely to lead to the start state. If several links are in the same importance category, the individual scales (also given previously) within that

---

Control relations: < Positive control relations; Negative control relations>

Positive control relations: <cause-effect enablement control>
Negative control relations: <limiting preventing interrupting terminating>

Temporal relations: <precede same-time-as>

Correspondence or analogical relations: equivalent-to/proportional
(no ranking)

Figure 6.17: Links between events

---

category are checked and a link is chosen. As an example, within the control category, a causal link is preferred over an enablement link.

An example of this procedure is shown in Figure 6.18, where the main path for the loudspeaker is searched for. The events that are being considered while searching for the main path are shown in italics, while the event-links are in bold face. The portion of the knowledge base corresponding to the loudspeaker is shown in Figure 6.19, with the various event-link types identified.

Right now, TAILOR searches for the main path any time it is required to do so. Minor changes to the program would allow this main path to be stored in the object frame to avoid having to recompute it each time it is needed. Note that finding the main path for the process trace plays a similar function as far as constructing text is concerned as the TEXT system's construction of the relevant knowledge pool (McKeown, 1985), since it delineates the part of the knowledge base used to generate a text.

Marking the side links/chains   Side links are put aside while searching for the main path and marked afterwards. While traversing the most important event-links for which the event under consideration is the object, the program keeps all the other links on hold. After the main path is found, all the other links are examined and tagged as possible side links or side chains. For example, in Figure 6.18, the link corresponding to the analogical link *"soundwaves-intensity varies* CORRESPONDS TO *current varies"* was put on hold while searching for the main path. Once the main path had been found, TAILOR marked this link as a side link.

Once all the potential side links have been found, they are counted. If there are many, they will be grouped at the end of the process explanation instead of being mentioned as part of the explanation. (This corresponds to diagram (3), in Figure 4.14 page 73, in Chapter 4.) A parameter indicates the value of *many*. If the number of side links is

127

Purpose slot: *changes current into soundwaves*

The goal and start states are taken from the purpose slot:

<u>Goal state</u>: *Soundwaves-intensity varies*
<u>Start state</u>: *current varies*

Searching for the main path starting from the goal:

Soundwaves-intensity varies: participates in two event-links:
    diaphragm vibrates **causes** *soundwaves-intensity varies*
    soundwaves-intensity varies **corresponds to** *current varies*

cause is chosen over **corresponds to** based on the importance link;

The search continues with the event *diaphragm vibrates.*

diaphragm vibrates: participates in one event-link:
    field varies **causes** *diaphragm vibrates*

The search continues with the event *field varies.*

field varies: participates in one event-link:
    current varies **causes** *field varies.*

The search continues with the event *current varies.* This is the start, the search ends. The main path is:

current varies **causes** *field varies.*
field varies **causes** *diaphragm vibrates.*
diaphragm vibrates **causes** *soundwaves-intensity varies.*

Figure 6.18: Finding the main path for the loudspeaker

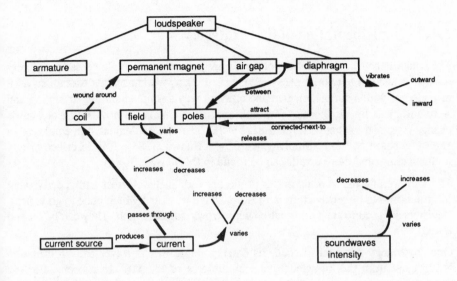

  → Relations (functional and physical)
  < Indicates that the relation has substeps
  ─ Links in the parts hierarchy

Links between events:

[current varies]*	causes	[field varies]
[current increases]	causes	[field increases]
[current decreases]	causes	[field decreases]
[field varies]*	causes	[diaphragm vibrates]
[field increases]	causes	[poles attract diaphragm]
[poles attract diaphragm]	causes	[diaphragm moves inward]
[field decreases]	causes	[poles release diaphragm]
[poles release diaphragm]	causes	[diaphragm moves outward]
[diaphragm vibrates]*	causes	[soundwave intensity varies]
[diaphragm moves inward]	causes	[soundwave intensity decreases]
[diaphragm moves outward]	causes	[soundwave intensity increases]
[diaphragm vibrates]	causes	[soundwave intensity varies]
[soundwave intensity varies]	corresponds-to	[current varies]

(Events marked with an asterisk (*) are on the main path)

Figure 6.19: Subset of the knowledge base for the loudspeaker

129

higher than the parameter, a flag is set. This flag is used to decide whether to include a side link or not while describing the main path.

6.4.3 Implementation of the Strategies

The constituency schema and the process trace strategies are implemented using augmented transition networks (ATN) (Woods, 1973).[4] We chose this formalism as it provided us with a simple, elegant and efficient way to implement our strategies, and were sufficient for our needs. (We will discuss in Chapter 8 how, when our needs changed, we had to change formalism as well.) The ATN implementation employed in TAILOR is based on TEXT's implementation (McKeown, 1985). It is described briefly in this section, and more details can be found in (McKeown, 1985).

The arcs joining the various nodes in the network include a test and specify what information is to be retrieved from the knowledge base, and which node to go to next. Registers are used to save information while traversing the graph. They can be set and tested.

Once a strategy has been chosen, its corresponding ATN is traversed. Information is retrieved from the knowledge base as the arcs of the ATN are chosen. For the constituency schema, the ATN arcs represent the rhetorical predicates of the schema. So traversing the ATN corresponds to filling the schema, matching the predicates against the knowledge base. For the process trace, the arcs are not rhetorical predicates but directives on how to traverse the event-links in the knowledge base.

Each time an arc is taken, and a proposition is obtained, that corresponds roughly to a sentence in the text to be generated. A proposition is either an instantiation of a rhetorical predicate (as dictated by the predicate semantics), or a value obtained from following a directive (from the process trace). When an arc is a rhetorical predicate, the *predicate argument* is the object the predicate is applied to, and the *predicate value* is the value retrieved from the knowledge base when the predicate is applied to an object.

A proposition contains values from the knowledge base, and is represented in a predicate-value form: the predicate is the name of the arc taken (i.e., either a rhetorical predicate or one of the directives). The value that was retrieved from the knowledge base when the arc was taken follows. Finally, some focus information is included. Focus information indicates which item is the focused item for the proposition. It used both in deciding among several potential propositions and in choosing syntactic structure and lexical items to translate the proposition in English. Both aspects will be explained later. In the case of a rhetorical predicate, the proposition also contains the entity the predicate is applied to, that is the *predicate argument*.

Examples of propositions are shown in Figures 6.20 and 6.21. While propositions use unique identifiers to refer to object frames, events and event-links, the corresponding

---

[4] Augmented transition networks are networks that include arbitrary tests on the arcs and registers to save information. Actions performed after taking an arc can set registers, while the tests on the arcs can set or test these registers.

English names are provided in both figures for clarity. Figure 6.20 presents propositions resulting from matching the constituency and identification predicates against the knowledge base. In both cases, the predicate argument is the *telephone*. The first element of the proposition is the name of the predicate. Its argument follows, that is, the object the predicate was applied to. The list following the predicate argument is the predicate value retrieved from the knowledge base for this object. Finally, the last element of the proposition is its focus.

Figure 6.21 shows a proposition resulting from following an event-link. This is indicated by the marker *process* as the first element of the proposition. The link that was retrieved follows, including both subject and object events. Finally, as in the previous examples, the proposition also includes its focus.

When the fact is retrieved from the knowledge base and included in the description, it is marked so that it will not be repeated later.

ATN Arc types The arcs of the ATN in TAILOR can be of several types. The arc types used for the strategy implementation are the same as those used for the schema implementation in TEXT. They are:

- *Fill <predicate or directive>*: This arc retrieves information from the knowledge base. In TEXT, this arc was used to instantiate a predicate by matching it against the knowledge base. In TAILOR, it is used to either instantiate a predicate or to give a directive on how to trace the knowledge base. The result of this arc is a proposition that is included in the description to be generated.

- *Jump <state>*: Jump to a specified state (without fetching anything from the knowledge base). When considering this arc, the ATN driver simulates the jump and thus computes the result of traversing its successors (i.e., the arcs from the state indicated in the jump arc).

- *Subr <subroutine-state>*: This arc specifies to start a subnetwork (or subroutine). Subnets are included only to simplify the graph. They could be included in the main graph. The subr arc would then be simply a jump to a state. A detailed description of how subroutines (and recursive calls) are handled can be found in (McKeown, 1985) and will not be included here.

- *Subr-end*: indicates the end of the subnet. The ATN driver returns to the state following the state that called the subnet in the main graph.

- *Push*: recursive call to a net. Before traversing this net, all the registers are saved, and new values may be given to the registers.

- *Pop*: indicates the end of a recursive call. The values of the registers are restored.

The arcs can have pre-actions, a test and post-actions. Pre-actions are performed before an arc is taken. They can reset registers (in case of a recursive call for example) or

Propositions corresponding to matching the *constituency* **and** *identification* **predicate against the knowledge base.**

The predicate argument is the object the predicate is applied to.

The predicate value is the information retrieved from the knowledge base when the predicate is applied to an object.

The default *focus* for the proposition is the object the predicate is applied to (its argument).

```
PREDICATE        ARGUMENT        PREDICATE VALUE

((Constituency   telephone   (transmitter, housing, line, receiver)
                             FOCUS: telephone)
```

English translation: *The telephone has a transmitter, a housing, a line and a receiver.*

```
PREDICATE        ARGUMENT           PREDICATE VALUE    FOCUS

((Identification telephone          (device)          telephone)
```

English translation: *The telephone is a device.*

Figure 6.20: Examples of propositions obtained from traversing an arc of the constituency schema

Proposition corresponding to one of the directives (*next causal link*) for following the event-links in the knowledge base. The default focus for the proposition is the event-link.

```
                    ((Process
Subject Event:      <person speaks-into transmitter>
Link:               &mr0 [causes]
Object Event:       <soundwaves hit diaphragm>)
Focus:              &mr0)
```

English translation: A person speaking into the transmitter causes soundwaves to hit the diaphragm.

Figure 6.21: Example of a proposition obtained from traversing an arc of the process trace

retrieve the possible foci to be used by the functions that fetch information from the knowledge base. Tests are performed in order to decide whether an arc is appropriate or not. Tests are arbitrary LISP functions. They often test registers or values contained in the predicate argument frame. Post-actions are executed once an arc has been chosen. For a fill arc, post-actions typically add the new proposition to the message constructed so far, mark the item retrieved from the knowledge base to avoid repetition, and update registers. Most arcs include a post-action that indicates which state to go next.

Traversing the graph The control structure of the ATN driver can be summarized as follows:

1. Retrieve all arcs emanating from a state.

2. Compute the test for each arc; save the arcs with successful tests.

3. For each arc saved:

   (a) Perform its pre-actions;

   (b) Match the arc against the knowledge base;

   This results in a pool of possible propositions.

4. Choose one proposition (i.e., one arc) among this pool. This step will be discussed after presenting what information is retrieved from the knowledge base for each type of fill arc.

5. Perform its post-actions (e.g., mark the item just retrieved from the knowledge base). One of the post-actions is a jump to the next state.

6. Go back to 1, starting with the next state.

Because of the availability of facts in the knowledge base and the fact that the ATN contains several options, we did not encounter the need to have the system backtrack after it has chosen an arc because it reached a blocked state. Backtracking could be done if necessary as the whole text is constructed before being generated. (Note that it would also be possible to generate as propositions are retrieved from the knowledge base, although this would make backtracking much harder.) Backtracking would require keeping a record of what has been used in a register instead of marking the used item in the knowledge base as is done now.

6.4.4 Stepping through the Constituency Schema

The arcs of the ATN for the constituency schema correspond to the predicates of the schema. The rhetorical predicates define the type of information to be retrieved from the knowledge base. The ATN corresponding to the constituency schema, now shown with its switches to the process trace, is given in Figure 6.22.

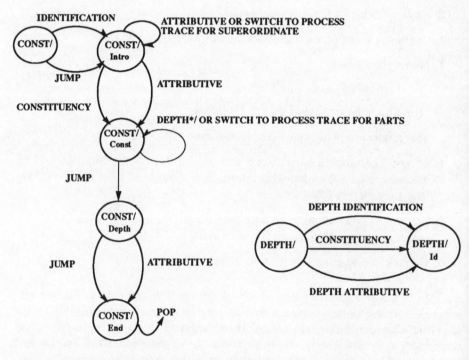

Figure 6.22: Constituency Schema and its ATN

The first predicate indicated in the schema, identification, is optional. It is thus possible to go from state CONST/ to CONST/*Intro* either by taking the arc labeled *identification* or with simply a jump to CONST/*Intro*, in which case the identification predicate is skipped. There, it is possible to include some attributive information about the object, or to switch to the process trace for the superordinate, if the identification predicate was taken. The *constituency* predicate then immediately. The *constituency* predicate dictates to present the subparts of an object. This is possible when the object has parts, that is when the object is *composite*. To allow for *unitary* objects, the schema was slightly changed by adding another alternative, the arc labeled *attributive*. This arc is taken only for unitary objects, that is, objects that do not have any subparts. This is indicated in the arc test. This test looks at the object frame to determine its type and decides which arc (attributive or constituency) is appropriate. If the *constituency* arc is taken, a register that indicates the subparts is set. This register will be used to supply more information about each part in turn.

After taking either of these arcs, the ATN driver then considers the next state, CONST/*Const*. At that point, one of three predicates can be taken for each subpart included in the parts register: *depth-identification*, *constituency* or *depth-attributive*. When there are no more parts in this register (it gets updated each time an arc is taken), the state CONST/*Depth* is reached. There, a jump arc or the arc labeled *attributive* is chosen. The schema ends and the constructed text is returned.

Predicate Semantics   Predicate semantics are implemented using functions that actually fetch the appropriate information. It is possible for a predicate to match several facts in the knowledge base. This is the case, for example, for the *attributive* predicate which provides properties or structural attributes about an object. In that case, all possible matches are retrieved, each forming a different proposition that gets added to the pool of potential propositions. After all the potential propositions have been formed, directives are applied to choose the most appropriate one.

As mentioned in Chapter 3 , propositions corresponding to several predicates were sometimes merged into one sentence at the surface level. This can be done using a sophisticated interface capable of combining two or more propositions. Not having such an interface, TAILOR simulates this output by allowing the semantics of some predicates to retrieve more information than strictly required by the linguistic predicates. For example, the constituency predicate dictates to retrieve the parts of an object. In TAILOR's implementation of the function corresponding to this predicate, properties associated with the parts can also be retrieved. Figure 6.23 illustrates this phenomenon.

In the first sentence of (1) in Figure 6.23, the function corresponding to the constituency predicate simply retrieves the parts of the object. In the second sentence, the depth-attributive predicate is applied to the parts, and we obtain attributive information about the diaphragm. In (2), parts are immediately retrieved with their properties. The same information as in (1) is conveyed, though in a more compact form.

Global flags determine whether TAILOR is allowed to collapse propositions. It is also possible to turn them off and obtain single sentence production for each proposition.

135

1. Apply the constituency predicate to *the microphone.* **Then, apply** *depth-attributive* **to the parts:**

> The microphone has a diaphragm and a system.
> The diaphragm is disc-shaped and aluminum.
> The system is doubly-resonant.

2. Apply the constituency predicate to *the microphone,* **with properties of parts allowed:**

> The microphone has a disc-shaped aluminum diaphragm and a doubly-resonant system.

Figure 6.23: Including more information than strictly required by the predicates

Figure 6.24 gives examples of the semantics of each predicate, with the different options available.

The identification predicate retrieves the superordinate of an object in the generalization hierarchy. With the appropriate flags on, it is possible to obtain at the same time the purpose of the object, as illustrated in 1.2 in Figure 6.24. The constituency predicate retrieves the subparts on an object (see 2.1 in the Figure), and it is also possible to include properties (as in 2.2) and purposes (as in 2.3). The attributive predicate matches attributes of the object. This includes properties such as material and shape (as in 3.1), and structural relations relating the current object with previously mentioned objects, (as in 3.2). Note that structural relations involve several objects. It is thus possible for a relation to match the attributive predicate with several different arguments (all the objects that take a part in that structural relations). A text produced from stepping through the constituency schema is shown in Figure 6.25.

6.4.5 The ATN corresponding to the Process Trace

In Chapter 4, we presented the process strategy in detail. In particular, we described all the different side link structures that might occur and specified how they should be treated. For each of these structures, there is an arc in the ATN. The process trace as explained in Chapter 4 only referred to producing a causal explanation of the device's mechanism. An introductory statement is actually also included in the strategy, in order to not immediately start the description with a causal relationship. This is represented in the ATN with the first arc, labeled *identification.* The other arcs of the ATN for the process trace dictate how to traverse the event-links contained in the knowledge base in order to produce a coherent process description. The first step in this process explanation is to find the main path. This step was explained earlier in this chapter. Given the main path, a list of event-links, the process trace mainly traces each link

Identification:
1.1 (identification &mem1 (device))
The transmitter is a microphone.

Purpose of the object allowed:
1.2 (identification &mem1(device)
(used-for (&rel27 &mem17 &mem19)))
The microphone is a device that changes soundwaves into current.

Constituency:
2.1 (constituency &mem1 ((&mem4) (&mem11)))
The microphone has a diaphragm and a system.

Including subparts properties:
2.2 (constituency &mem1 ((&mem4 (property (shape disc)
(material aluminum)))
(&mem11 (property
(type doubly-resonant))))))
The microphone has a disc-shaped aluminum diaphragm and a
doubly-resonant system.

Including subparts purposes when available:
2.3 (constituency &mem1 ((&mem4)
(&mem11 (used-for
(&rel8 &mem11 &mem21)))))
The microphone has a diaphragm and a system to broaden the response.

Attributive:

Retrieving properties:
3.1 (attributive &mem4
(property (shape disc) (material aluminum)))
The diaphragm is disc-shaped and aluminum.

Retrieving structural relations:
3.2 (attributive &mem4 (relation (&rel7 &mem4 &mem34)))
The diaphragm is mounted on the poles of the magnet.

Figure 6.24: Predicate semantics

Loudspeaker

TAILOR Output:

The loudspeaker changes current into soundwaves. It has a large thin dome-shaped paper diaphragm, a ring-shaped permendur armature, a coil, a ring-shaped permanent magnet and a gap. The diaphragm is mounted on the poles of the magnet. The gap contains air. The gap is between the poles and the diaphragm. The coil is mounted on the magnet.

Figure 6.25: Description using the Constituency Schema

---

at a time. The ATN corresponding to the process trace was shown in Figure 4.20 in Chapter 4. It is repeated in shown in Figure 6.26. Its arcs are:

- *Identification*: This is identical to the identification predicate in the constituency schema. Here, the device is identified with its function.

- *Side-chain1?*: This corresponds to the side link structure shown in diagram 1-b of Figure 4.7, in Chapter 4, page 67. There is a long side link that is not initiated from the main path but is re-attached to the main path at a later point. This link needs to be included if it is an enabling (or causal) condition for an event on the main path. The link is traversed before starting the main path.

- *Next-main-link*: The main path consists of several event-links. This directive indicates to take the next link on the main path. When the arc is taken, the link is taken off the list that contains the events on the main path. Each time a link is taken, all the parts that are mentioned in the events are collected, so that attributive information might be given about each of them.

- *Side-chain2?*: This corresponds to the side link structure shown in diagram 1-a of Figure 4.7, in Chapter 4, page 67. There is a long side link that comes off the main path at event (1) and gets reattached to the main path at a later point. The link is mentioned when event (1) has been introduced.

- *Side-link?*: This corresponds to diagrams 2-a and 2-b of Figure 4.11, in Chapter 4, page 71, where a short side link is included as part of the process explanation. A test on the arcs makes sure that the register that indicates that there are too many short side links to include them as part of the process explanation is not set.

- *Attributive*: This arc is similar to the attributive predicate of the constituency schema. However, this predicate is given one constraint, that of retrieving only properties about the object, not structural relations. This was decided as it seems that it produces better descriptions for a naive user. The predicate is applied to all the parts that were just mentioned as part of the process explanation.

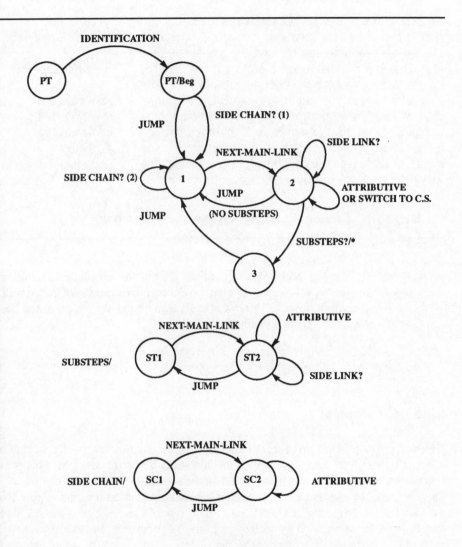

Figure 6.26: ATN corresponding to the Process Trace

Oscillator (generated by TAILOR)

An oscillator is a device that produces a varying current, when a battery produces a current. Because the battery produces the current, the transistor turns on. That the transistor turns on is caused also by the capacitor discharging through the resistor. The transistor turning on causes the capacitor to charge. This causes the transistor to turn off. Because the transistor turns off, the capacitor discharges through the resistor. The resistor has low resistance. The capacitor discharging through the resistor causes the varying current to be produced.	identification next-main-link short-side-link-back next-main-link next-main-link next-main-link attributive next-main-link

Figure 6.27: Description using the Process Trace

- *Substeps?*: This arc checks whether the event just mentioned is decomposable. If it is and the substeps do not involve basic concepts the user does not understand, the substeps are followed. The test actually also checks the length of the text generated so far to avoid producing very long texts.

A text generated by traversing the ATN of the process trace is shown in Figure 6.27.

6.4.6 Choosing an arc

Given a pool of possible propositions, one must be eventually chosen. This decision is partially based on the focus information contained in the proposition. This thus implements another local constraint, based on the content of the knowledge base and the previous discourse. Focus information is used to keep a text as coherent as possible by making sure propositions are related to each other in some ways. TAILOR uses the focus guidelines defined by McKeown in the TEXT system. In TEXT, McKeown adapted for generation the focus rules Sidner (1979) had identified for use in discourse analysis. These focus guidelines, which are described in detail in (McKeown, 1985), dictate to choose, in order:

1. a proposition whose focus is among items (or concepts) that were just introduced in the previous proposition

2. a proposition with the same focus as the previous proposition

3. a proposition whose focus was the focus of a past proposition (an item previously discussed).

Focus information must be maintained in registers for these decisions to be made. The registers are updated after each proposition is added to the text to be generated.

In TAILOR, focus information alone, however, rarely constrains the decision process totally, and a choice is made based on other factors. One factor used in TAILOR is the availability of lexical choice. This is similar to (Meteer, 1990) where Meteer argues that lexical choice must be made before a text plan is decided upon to ensure its expressibility. In TAILOR, however, lexical selection is not *made* at that point, but its expressibility *is* ensured (Paris, 1988) by making sure lexical items to express the proposition are available. This is the case in particular for the attributive predicate. As mentioned previously, it is possible for a relation to match the attributive predicate with several different arguments, that is with the focus on several different items. To decide when it might be appropriate to include this specific fact from the knowledge base, the textual component calls the dictionary interface to check whether the system has a lexical item for this relation that would place the focus on the required focused item. If no such lexical item can be found, the relation is not chosen for the item.

As an example, consider the relation *the air gap is between the poles and the diaphragm*. This relation matches the attributive predicate when the predicate is applied to any of the three items involved in the relation: the gap, the poles and the diaphragm. It is only when the relation is applied to the gap, however, that the dictionary interface returns an English word for the relation, that places the focus on the predicate argument. For the two other items, no lexical choice can be found with the required focus. As a result, this relation is chosen only when the predicate is applied to the gap. This is the only interaction between the textual component and the surface generator in TAILOR, where the surface structure and lexical choice affects the organization of the text.

Another factor involved in the decision process in TAILOR is making sure that a relation is mentioned only after all its constituents have already been introduced. For example, before including an analogical link between two relations, it is preferable to have first introduced the two events that are related by the analogical link. This is illustrated in Figure 6.28.

6.5   The Interface

TAILOR's interface takes as input the content of the description from the textual component and assigns lexical items to the various concepts contained in the description. The output of the interface is a functional description of the sentence to be generated. This functional description can be fed into a surface generator that will unify the input with a functional grammar to produce English. The output of the interface must be in the same formalism as that of the functional grammar. Figure 6.29 shows an example of an input to the interface and the output that is be produced.

The analogical link "the soundwaves vary like the current" is included without checking whether both events have already been introduced:

> The current varies, like the intensity varies. The variation of the current causes the field of the magnet to vary. This causes the diaphragm to vibrate. The vibration of the diaphragm causes the intensity of the soundwaves to vary.

A more appropriate text would be:

> The variation of the current causes the field of the magnet to vary. This causes the diaphragm to vibrate. The vibration of the diaphragm causes the intensity of the soundwaves to vary. The intensity varies, like the current varies.

Figure 6.28: When to include a relation

Interface Input:
```
((identification &mem1 (device)) &mem1)
```

Interface Output:
```
((cat s)
 (verb ((v === be)))
 (goal ((n === device) (article === indef))))
```

English that would be generated after unification with the grammar:

> The telephone is a device.

Figure 6.29: Interface input and output

The interface uses a lexicon to retrieve the lexical item(s) associated with entities, relations, or event-links. This lexicon is the same as the one used by RESEARCHER in parsing texts. Syntactic information and constraints were added to the original lexicon. The syntactic information mainly indicates the part of speech of the item, as this is needed to construct the sentence. Constraints are indicated by a test. This test is an arbitrary function that is used either to test the appropriateness of the lexical item (possibly based on focus information) or to return syntactic constraints (such as "this verb must be used with the preposition *to*.)" The interface uses focus information and previously mentioned items to decide on articles. Focus information is included in the output of the interface, as it will also be used in the surface generator to decide on the verb voice (passive or active).

The interface is highly modular and regular. Frames of the same types are always translated in the same way, and the structure of the sentence to be generated is usually dictated and constrained by the predicate of the proposition.

For example, in Figure 6.29, the proposition resulted from applying the *identification* predicate to the object frame &mem1. Because of the identification predicate, the verb *to be* was chosen by the interface. Once the main verb of the sentence was selected, the verb roles are filled by the other elements of the proposition. In the figure, as &mem1 is the predicate argument, its corresponding English word, the telephone becomes the subject, or protagonist, of the verb. Device, the predicate value (i.e., the fact retrieved from the knowledge base when *identification* was applied to the telephone), becomes the object, or goal. The determiners are chosen depending on whether a particular item has already been mentioned or whether the item is the object of the description. After having decided on the translation for the predicate of the proposition, the interface calls itself recursively to assign lexical items to the predicate argument and value, and fills the appropriate roles.

The predicate of the proposition constrains the syntactic structure of the sentences as indicated in Figure 6.30. The identification predicate is always translated into the verb *to be*. The predicate argument becomes the subject of the verb, while the predicate value becomes the object. This is illustrated in Figure 6.31.

The constituency predicate is always translated into the verb *have*. The predicate argument is the subject of the sentence as for the identification predicate. The predicate value, here the constituents, form the object of the verb.

The attributive predicate is translated into the verb *to be* when the predicate value is one or more properties about the object. These properties are translated into adjectives. If the predicate value is a structural relation, (i.e., a relation record), the interface is called recursively with the relation record to form a sentence. A relation record is always translated into a sentence, where the relation dictates the verb. A lexical item is chosen for a relation, usually depending on the focus of the proposition. For example, in the relation <*the gap contains air*>, if the focus of the proposition is on the *gap*, the verb *contains* will be chosen. However, if the focus is on *air*, the verb *to be* is chosen together with the preposition *inside of*. The chosen lexical item and the focus of the proposition thus dictates how to construct the sentence and fill the other constituents.

143

Identification predicate: Verb = be
                    Protagonist = item the predicate was applied to
                    Goal = information retrieved from the knowledge
                        base (superordinate of the object)

Constituency predicate: Verb = have
                    Protagonist = item the predicate was applied to
                    Goal = information retrieved from the knowledge
                        base (constituents of the object)

Attributive predicate:
  1) Information retrieved from the knowledge base are properties
                    Verb = be
                    Protagonist = item the predicate was applied to
                    Goal = adjectives (for the properties retrieved)
                        from the knowledge base

  2) Information retrieved from the knowledge base is a structural relation
                    Call the interface to translate the structural
                        relation, i.e., the relation record.

Relation record: Verb = English word corresponding to the relation
                        frame
                    Protagonist and Goal: depend on the syntactic
                        information indicated in the lexicon for the
                        lexical item chosen.

Process link: a complex sentence constructed around the
                    translation of the link and that of the two events
                    related by the link.

Figure 6.30: Translation of the various propositions

Proposition: ((identification &mem43 (&mem20)) &mem43)

Identification predicate → verb = be
                          subject &mem43 [telephone transmitter]
                          object &mem20 [microphone]

Structure formed: ((cat s) (verb ((v === be)))
                             (prot ((n=== transmitter)
                                    (article === def)))
                             (goal ((n === microphone)
                                    (article === indef)))))

Corresponding English: The transmitter is a microphone

Figure 6.31: Constructing a sentence from the identification predicate

The translation for the attributive predicate is illustrated in Figure 6.32.

All relations (whether structural or functional) are systematically translated into *simple* sentences.

Finally, most process links (event-links) are translated into complex sentences. As a process link relates two events, each of which is a functional relation, each event is translated at first into a simple sentence of the kinds shown above. A complex sentence is then formed by joining the two sentences based on the event link in a variety of ways. For example, there are a number of ways a cause-effect relation can be expressed:

- Using the explicit verb *cause*, as in "the current varying causes the soundwaves to vary."

- Using a subordinate, introduced by the subordinator *because*, as in "because the current varies the soundwaves vary." This sentence can also be expressed by reversing the order of the main clause and subordinate to get "the soundwaves vary because the current varies."

- Using a subordinate, introduced by the subordinator *when*, as in "when the current varies, the soundwaves vary." As in the previous case, the order of the two clauses can be reversed.

- Using the noun form of the verb if possible, as in "the variation of the current causes the soundwave to vary."

145

Proposition:
    `((attributive &mem13 (properties (size small))) &mem13`

Identification predicate → verb = be
                          subject: &mem13 [diaphragm]
                          adjectival phrase: small

Structure formed: ((cat s) (verb ((v === be)))
                              (prot ((n=== diaphragm)
                                    (article === def)))
                              (ap ((adj === small))))

Corresponding English: The diaphragm is small

Proposition:
    `((attributive [gap] (&rel43 [contain] [gap] [air])) [gap])`

    `&rel43` → verb = contain

Structure formed: ((cat s) (verb ((v === contain)))
                              (prot ((n=== gap) (article === def)))
                              (goal ((n === air))))

Corresponding English: The gap contains air

Proposition:
    `((attributive [air] (&rel43 [contain] [gap] [air])) [air])`

    `&rel43` → verb = be, with the preposition "inside of"

Structure formed: ((cat s) (verb ((v === be))
                              (pp ((prep === inside-of)
                                    (n === gap)
                                    (article === def)))))
                            (prot ((n=== air))))

Corresponding English: The air is inside of the gap

Figure 6.32: Constructing a sentence from the attributive predicate

The interface is able to combine two simple sentences in all ways shown above. Because of extensions performed on the grammar, the interface only needs to specify the type of complex sentence desired, and the actual complex sentence is constructed by the grammar. As an example, to use a subordinate introduced with the subordinator *because*, the interface need only to form, from the two simple sentences, the structure shown in Figure 6.33. "Embed" is used in the protagonist and goal to indicate that the constituent is a sentence. The two features "surface" and "order" indicate the structure of the desired output. To translate an event-link, the interface translates the two events separately as simple relation records and joins them together by adding the desired features. If no features are added, the grammar defaults to the following construction: "the soundwaves varying causes the current to vary".

A subordinate clause introduced with the subordinator "when" is used to indicate the beginning of a substep chain. When several forms are available, the interface keeps track of the last form used and employs each form in turn for variety. To add to the quality of the texts generated, the interface also makes note of the last event that was mentioned. This allows it to use the pronoun "this" when it is possible, as illustrated in Figure 6.34.

Finally, objects are translated into the appropriate nouns. Sometimes, two different objects have the same English translation. To be able to unambiguously refer to them, the interface keeps a list of all the objects that are mentioned in the text. If two objects have the same English translation, the interface tries to disambiguate them, by including their respective properties. For example, the dialing mechanism has two gears, one small and one large, connected to each other. The translation "the gear is connected to the gear" is clearly ambiguous. By adding the properties associated with each object, "the small gear is connected to the large gear" is obtained, and each item is identified unambiguously. While simple, this disambiguation technique has been successful in TAILOR. This technique would not be adequate as a general disambiguation technique as it would break down if the objects had the same properties, in which case another way to differentiate the two objects would be required.

6.6 The surface generator

The surface generator takes the output of the interface and produces English. The surface generator used in TAILOR is based on that of TEXT and uses a Functional Unification Grammar (FUG) as defined by (Kay, 1979). The input is unified with the grammar to produce English.

The functional grammar was chosen because of its availability and its "clean" formalism. The functional grammar is represented in a declarative form. Because of the separation of the functional grammar and the unifier (the program that unifies the grammar and the input to produce English), it is possible to change or augment the grammar without having to change any of the unifier's code. Moreover, using the functional grammar, various constraints can be directly encoded in the grammar, thus simplifying

Proposition to translate:
```
<the soundwaves vary> causes <the current varies>
```

1) each event is translated into a simple sentence:

    ((cat s)   (verb ((v === vary)))
              (prot ((n === soundwave) (number plur)
                   (article === def))))

    ((cat s)   (verb ((v === vary)))
              (prot ((n === current) (article === def))))

2) construct the complex sentence by specifying to the grammar the construction desired: a subordinate, introduced with the subordinator because.

    ((cat s)
       (surface because) (order front)
       (verb ((v === cause)))
       (prot
         ((embed ((cat s)   (verb ((v === vary)))
                            (prot ((n === soundwave) (number plur)
                                 (article === def)))))
       (goal
         ((embed ((cat s)   (verb ((v === vary)))
                            (prot ((n === current)
                                 (article === def))))))

Figure 6.33: Combining simple sentences into a complex sentence

Suppose we had the two event-links:

> The soundwave intensity increasing **causes** the diaphragm to spring forward. The diaphragm springing forward **causes** the granules to be compressed.

By keeping track of the last mentioned event, the interface can replace the subject of an event link by the pronoun *this*:

> The soundwave intensity increasing **causes** the diaphragm to spring forward. This **causes** the granules to be compressed.

Figure 6.34: Using the pronoun *this* in a process explanation

the interface that constructs the input to the grammar. For example, one constraint can state that the verb voice is dependent on the focus of the sentence (Kay, 1979; McKeown, 1985). These global constraints can be represented separately from syntactic rules, so that they need to be stated only once; this is not the case in other formalisms – see (McKeown and Paris, 1987; McKeown and Elhadad, 1991). Finally, as the input is unified in the grammar, many syntactic details can be included in the grammar and the input simplified. This further simplifies the interface. As an example, the input to the grammar need not specify the number of the verb.

6.6.1 The functional grammar and the unification process

As the grammar and the unification process are described in detail in (McKeown, 1985; McKeown and Elhadad, 1991; Elhadad, 1991; Elhadad, 1992), we will describe them only very briefly here.

The functional grammar is called a functional description (FD). It is made of attribute-value pairs. Each attribute-value pair is itself a functional description and can also be formed of other FD's. The whole grammar contains subgrammars for each possible syntactic category, such as *sentence, noun phrase or np* and *verb group*.

A simple subgrammar for noun phrases (NP) is shown in Figure 6.35. Alternatives (*alt*) specify that there are several ways to form a constituent. For example, in the figure, there are two alternatives, one of which will be chosen depending whether the noun phrase of the input has an article or not. Each alternative contains a few attribute-value pairs.

The *patterns* indicate the order in which the constituents should appear in the English output. For example, in thus figure, the pattern in the second alternative specifies that the article is to occur before the noun (nnp). *Dots* indicate that other constituents may occur at that place. In this example, the pattern indicates that it is possible for other constituents to occur before the article and after the noun.

```
((cat np)
 (alt
  (
    ((article none)
     (pattern (dots nnp dots)))
    ((article any)
     (article ((cat article) (lex any)))
     (pattern (dots article nnp dots)))))
    (nnp ((cat nnp)))))
```

Figure 6.35: A simple subgrammar for noun phrases

The input is represented in the same formalism as the grammar. As an example, the input representing a noun phrase might be:

```
((cat np)  (n   telephone)
           (article def))
```

This input would be unified with the subgrammar shown in the figure and the English noun phrase "the telephone" would be produced. Examples of input to the grammar have already been given in Figures 6.29, 6.31, 6.32, 6.33.

TAILOR's grammar grew out of one used in TEXT and was extended to support more syntactic constructions and to include more constraints on choices, thus simplifying the interface. Our extensions to TEXT grammar mainly involved complex constructions.[5] In particular, more complex constructions have been added (Paris and Kwee, 1985; Kwee, 1987). These include subordinate sentences and embedded clauses; that is, a sentence embedded in a constituent. Both are needed to express relationships among events, as shown in Figure 6.36.

The grammar is able to construct a complex sentence from two simple ones, given explicit information on the structure to be used. This is important, as, in TAILOR, there is a great need for complex sentences to express process information. Explicitly constructing complex sentences in the interface is a tedious and complicated process. By having the grammar construct the complex sentence from simple sentences, the interface is greatly simplified. We showed in Figure 6.33 the input the interface needs to construct. All the various complex sentences mentioned previously can be constructed in the grammar in a similar manner. A default construction is also provided, in case no specification occurs in the input.

---

[5]The reader is referred to (Paris and Kwee, 1985) for our extensions to the grammar. For a large Functional Unification Grammar, see (Elhadad, 1991; Elhadad, 1992).

Event link to be expressed:
```
<the soundwaves vary> causes <the current varies>
```

Using a subordinate clause:
Because the soundwaves vary, the current varies.

Using an embedded clause:
The soundwaves varying causes the current to vary.

Figure 6.36: Embedded clauses and their use in TAILOR

Furthermore, besides constructing a complex sentence, the grammar is now able to use the noun form of a verb (whenever possible), resulting in a smoother text and greater variety of constructions. For example, instead of constructing a sentence from "the diaphragm vibrates" as one of the constituents of a complex sentence, the grammar is able to form the noun phrase "the vibration of the diaphragm." This is done in a similar way as combining simple sentences: the feature (trans verb-noun) needs to be added in the input. The grammar then checks its lexicon to see if it has a noun form for the verb. If it does not, the result is the default construction.

TAILOR's grammar contains a wide variety of complex sentences. However, the grammar can only process one sentence at a time and does not reason about discourse.

Given a grammar and an input, there are two steps in generating an English sentence: *unification* with the grammar, and *linearization* of the resulting structure. The input to the unification process is a deep structure of the sentence to be generated, produced by the interface (such as those shown in Figures 6.29, 6.31, 6.32, and 6.33). It typically does not contain all the syntactic information necessary to generate the sentence. This input is *unified* with the grammar and thus enriched with all necessary syntactic information, including information about the order in which constituents should appear in the sentence. The linearizer then takes this enriched input and produces a flat list, the English sentence. Morphology and punctuation is also performed in the linearizer.

The unification process unifies each functional description in the input with the grammar. To unify a functional description, the unifier considers each attribute-value pair in the grammar and unifies its value part with that of the corresponding attribute in the input if present. If an attribute occurs in the grammar but not in the input, the input is enriched with the attribute-value pair from the grammar. (That is, the resulting structure is the *union* of the input and the grammar.) The grammar is thus used to enrich the input with all the syntactic information necessary to produce a sentence.

151

6.7 Issues pertaining to domain dependency

In this chapter, we presented the implementation of the TAILOR system. The strategies described here, their corresponding ATN and the ATN driver can all be used in different systems. This is because rhetorical predicates and the directives are *independent* of any knowledge base. The test as to which strategy to employ when as well as the test on the specific arcs might need to be changed to reflect the change in domain and knowledge base. The functions that actually fetch the information from the knowledge base (i.e., the predicate semantics and the function that carry out the directives) are specific to the TAILOR system and its knowledge base and would have to be adapted in another domain. Similarly, the interface is dependent on the knowledge base in that each frame type requires a different syntactic construction. On the other hand, the surface generator, including the grammar and the unifier, is entirely domain independent and can be moved without any changes (except to the grammar lexicon).

Each of the components of TAILOR is modular, and interaction among them is limited to a few places. As a result, each could be transported separately and applied to another system. For example, the interface and the grammar could be replaced by the equivalent for another language. Similarly, the output of the textual component could be passed to a graphics generator interface instead of a natural language generator. Alternatively, the textual component could be augmented to address more question types or include more strategies. In that case, the interface might have to be augmented to reflect the addition of more predicates or directives, but much of it would remain. The functional grammar could also be still used. Note, however, that more interaction among the components might be necessary to produce smoother texts.

6.8 TAILOR as a question answering system

As the generation component of a question answering system TAILOR at this point has two main limitations:

1. As discussed in Chapter 1, we are only concerned here with generating descriptions. Thus TAILOR only handles requests for descriptions, in the form shown above. A full question answering system would have the capability to answer any question that might be asked, although descriptions are a good starting point.

2. TAILOR is not an interactive system and there is very little feedback from previous discourse. In TAILOR, the user issues a request for a description and the description is generated. The object that was just described is added into the user model, as TAILOR assumes the user now has local expertise about it. TAILOR does not keep a record of all the questions asked by the user and the answers provided. As a result, TAILOR cannot detect that a question is asked several times. In the next chapter, we show our current research effort which address this issue.

Chapter 7

Related Work

This section presents other research efforts aimed at providing answers appropriate for a given user (or a class of users). These efforts involve both generation and user modelling; some have more emphasis on obtaining the user model, others on generating answers taking a user model into consideration. Although many researchers are working on generation, we will only discuss generation work that is related to the work presented in this book. Research in reading comprehension and psychology is also of interest, as it provides insight into what might make an answer more understandable to users with different knowledge levels. This section is not meant to present in detail all the work related to the topic of this book, but to present an overview of other research efforts together with pointers to literature for the interested reader.

7.1 Related work in user modelling and generation

User modelling problems include the task of constructing and organizing a model. Constructing a user model can be done either by collecting information from a user, inferring facts from a dialogue, or a combination of both. User modelling also includes issues of exploiting the user model to improve the system's answering abilities. All these aspects are important, and an ideal system would incorporate all of them. In this section, we present some of the major research that addresses these issues, starting with Rich's work, as it has been the basis for many other systems.

7.1.1   Using stereotypes

Rich (1989) showed how a model of the user can be built by refining and intersecting various stereotypes and how a system can use such a model to tailor its answers to a user. GRUNDY, a system simulating a librarian, utilized this method to suggest books to its users.

GRUNDY had a generalization hierarchy of stereotypes, each containing a set of characteristics. Associated with a stereotype were *triggers* that signalled the appropriate use of a stereotype. Stereotypes were activated through these triggers when users were asked to describe themselves by typing a few words. Because of the generalization hierarchy, one stereotype could also activate another. The user model was built up by combining the characteristics of the active stereotypes. The user model thus contained a set of characteristics, taken from the active stereotypes. A *justification*, indicating from which stereotype the facet was borrowed, was associated with each characteristic, in case the system needed to remember how the information was derived.

Once the model was built, GRUNDY used it to select a book to present to the user. The most salient characteristics of the user were selected, and one was chosen at random to serve as a basis for selection. As the objects in the knowledge base (books) also had attributes that corresponded to the facets of the users' stereotypes, a set of books matching the chosen characteristic was selected. Each book of the set was then evaluated against the other salient characteristics of the user, and the best match was presented to the user.

GRUNDY also examined the user model to decide which aspects of the book to mention when presenting the book to the user. If the book was refused, GRUNDY would attempt to understand why by asking the user which characteristic of the book was disliked. Based on the answer, GRUNDY would try to alter the user model by changing the inappropriate characteristic.

The way TAILOR decides what to present to the user differs from GRUNDY's since it is not based on attributes attached to items in the knowledge base. TAILOR relies on no specific information in the database to tell it what is appropriate for a given type of user. Rather, it uses a more complex set of criteria to choose relevant facts to present to the user, based on a characterization of what type of knowledge is appropriate in light of the user's domain knowledge.

In building GRUNDY, Rich was mainly interested in building the user model. Although this is a very different emphasis from our work, and our user model is quite different from the one used in GRUNDY (as it contains explicit information about the user's domain knowledge instead of various facets borrowed from stereotypes), this work can provide the basis to build *initial approximations* of the user model which can be used until more detailed and explicit knowledge about the user can be gathered.

7.1.2 Modelling and exploiting the user's domain knowledge

Several researchers have already given their system the ability to tailor its answer to the user's knowledge about the domain of discourse, some at the content level, others at the phrasing level. We briefly present these research efforts.

Wallis and Shortliffe have used the naive/expert distinction in their work on providing explanations in the domain of medical expert systems (Wallis and Shortliffe, 1982). The inference rules employed by the expert system were given a complexity factor, and users were assigned expertise levels. To generate explanations, the causal chain corresponding to the system's behavior was passed to the generator. The complexity measure of each rule in the chain was matched against the user's level of expertise to determine whether the rule should be included in the explanation or not. This procedure resulted in giving more or less detail depending on the user's domain knowledge. As we have seen in our analysis, this is not the only factor which should be changed when tailoring a text to a user's level of expertise: a generator should also vary the *kind* of information to be presented.

In his work, Sleeman developed UMFE, a user modelling front end to be used to tailor expert systems' explanations (Sleeman, 1985). As in (Wallis and Shortliffe, 1982), UMFE receives from an expert system the causal chain of inference rules which were activated in deriving a conclusion. The rules are assigned complexity and importance factors. UMFE determines which rules to present to the user based on these factors and the expertise level of the user. The emphasis in UMFE is on determining the level of sophistication of the user. This is done both by questioning the user and by employing inference rules. These rules relate concepts to each other based on their complexity factors to suggest additional concepts the user might know. These rules allow UMFE to ask the user a minimal number of questions.

The chains of inference rules employed by these two expert systems are similar to the links used in TAILOR to generate a process trace. In both the program developed by Wallis and Shortliffe and UMFE, however, unlike in TAILOR, the content of the answer has already been decided upon by the time the user model is examined. The user model is utilized mainly to decide on the amount of detail to include in the explanation. The issue of whether the level of detail is the only important parameter to vary is not addressed. This is precisely the issue we confront in this work.

The CADHELP system, which serves as an interface to a Computer Aided Design system, is also sensitive to some extent to the user's level of expertise as it is verbose with a new user and omits information as the user gains experience with the system (Cullingford *et al.*, 1982). CADHELP does not keep a user model *per se*, however, but only remembers the previous discourse. There is no characterization about what kind of information should be included for which type of user. In a similar approach, Carenini and Moore (1993) take the previous discourse into consideration to plan utterances. This allows them, for example, to describe a concept by comparing it to another concept if this other concept was already described previously.

The HAM-ANS system has a model of the user's knowledge which is mainly used for resolution and production of anaphora (Jameson and Wahlster, 1982; Hoeppner *et al.*, 1984). When asked a question, the system attempts to produce the smallest unambiguous answer possible. By using the system's ellipsis and anaphora resolution component (with a feedback loop) and the user model, the system checks whether a potential ellipsis or anaphora will be understood by the user, given the user's knowledge about the discourse. If the system determines that the answer can be understood in the current context, the answer is produced. Otherwise, the system tries to elaborate on its answer. TAILOR differs from HAM-ANS in that it uses its user model to decide on the *content* of an answer and rather than *phrasing*.

More recently, Chin was concerned with modelling and obtaining the user's domain knowledge about the UNIX system (Chin, 1986; Chin, 1989). His system, KNOME, is part of UC, the UNIX Consultant (Wilensky *et al.*, 1984). KNOME uses stereotypes for both the users and the knowledge base, which is a set of UNIX commands. Stereotypes for the commands in the knowledge base include *simple, mundane* and *complex*, while users are divided into four groups: *novice, beginner, intermediate* and *expert*. Each user category is expected (with some certainty factor) to know about some class(es) of commands. Unlike UMFE, KNOME does not ask the user any questions but tries to deduce the user's domain knowledge from what the user includes (or does not include) in a question posed to UC. To do this, KNOME relies on both the stereotype system and a few inferencing rules about what the user is likely to know.[1] KNOME infers the user's level of expertise by combining all the evidence it has about which facts the user knows or does not know. UC employs KNOME to decide how to answer a question, typically by omitting from the answer what it assumes the user already knows. For instance, UC does not include the example associated with a command when explaining the command, unless the user has been determined to be novice. TAILOR, on the other hand, is able to not only *omit* information, but also include different type of information.

While KNOME's double stereotype system seems to be successful in the UC domain, it is not as applicable in the domain of complex devices, where it is hard to partition the knowledge base into a few categories and decide that knowing about one type of objects implies more expertise than knowing about another set of objects. For example, there is no reason to believe that knowing about microphones indicates more expertise about the domain of complex devices than knowing about telescopes. Another approach is thus required. Furthermore, we wanted to be able to tailor answers to users whose domain knowledge level falls anywhere along a knowledge spectrum without having to classify users into a few discrete stereotypes. Finally, in this work, we are more concerned with exploiting the user model whereas Chin was more concerned with building it.

---

[1]Nessen (1986) describes a system similar to KNOME, but in which the user model is continuously updated.

7.1.3 Using knowledge about the user's plans and goals to generate responses

A great deal of research is being conducted on determining users' plans and goals and using them to understand incomplete or incorrect sentences and generate helpful responses. Although we do not address this issue here, the user's goals can also play an important part in deciding what to include in an answer. Indeed, an answer for a user whose goal is to buy an object should include different kinds of information than an answer for a user who wants to repair this object. The ability to detect and address users' goals and plans is important and would need to be included in a full question answering system. We will therefore give a brief summary of the research done in this area of user modelling and generation, beginning with that of Allen and Perrault.

Allen and Perrault (1980) examined the problems of generating appropriate responses to questions by inferring the questioner's goal. They showed that, by keeping a model of the questioners' beliefs and by being able to infer their plans and goals, a system can provide helpful and cooperative answers, as it can detect obstacles in the users' plans and provide information that will help accomplishing the desired goal. They developed a method that enables a system to derive the user's beliefs and goals. Using this method, a question answering system can build a user model containing the user's goals and beliefs and use it to answer questions in a cooperative fashion. The types of cooperative answers a system would be able to generate using this model include direct and indirect answers, as well as answers containing more information than requested in the question.

To detect the user's goals and plans, a system needs domain knowledge that includes *plans* and *goals* users may have in the domain of discourse, a formulation of *actions*, which have preconditions, substeps and effects, and *beliefs* and *wants* (intentions). In their system, Allen and Perrault used a standard planning formalism to represent plans and goals (Fikes and Nilsson, 1971), in which given an *initial state of the world W* and a *goal G*, a *plan* is a sequence of actions that transform *W* into *G*. Plans were domain specific and were used to derive the goal of a questioner. Because this knowledge was represented explicitly, the system was able to reason about what the user needed to know in order to achieve a goal. This fact is important since a system appears to be cooperative when it is able to provide information that will help the user achieve a goal.

Research on plans and goals and their use in cooperative discourse has continued since Allen and Perrault's work. Further plan inferencing models have been developed to allow for more complex sets of goals and plans, e.g., (Carberry, 1983; Sidner, 1985; Litman and Allen, 1987; Carberry, 1990; Eller and Carberry, 1991; Raskutti and Zukerman, 1991; Cohen et al., 1991; Goodman and Litman, 1992; Mayfield, 1992), and to provide responses that are tailored to the user's goals and intentions (McKeown et al., 1985; McKeown, 1988; van Beek, 1987). Finally, many researchers are examining the problem of recognizing that a user's plan is incorrect and correcting it (e.g., (Sidner and Israel, 1981; Pollack, 1986; Quilici, 1989; Retz-Schmidt, 1991; Calistri-Yeh, 1991). Related work by Morik (1985, 1986) has looked at the problem of modelling a user's wants in order to produce cooperative responses (Morik, 1985; Morik, 1986).

Exploiting knowledge about the user's goals and plans as well as the user's domain knowledge to generate appropriate responses   More recently, some research has gone into reasoning about several aspects of a user model to generate an appropriate response. This work has been done mainly in the context of *task-oriented dialogues* and *tutoring environments*. Building on our work, Wolz (1990) uses a three-part user model, which contains a discourse context, that is the state goal of the user, the stated plans and details of the goal, a situational context, that is what the user is actually doing in the physical world, and the user's domain expertise, which indicate what the user knows (typically how to achieve a goal). With this model, Wolz's system is able to reason as to how to answer a question from the user to meet his or her needs. That is, her system will include information to help the user achieve his or her goal, and correct their knowledge of plans if that is necessary.

Similarly, Sarner and Carberry (1992) use a multifaceted model to provide tailored definitions. Their system takes into consideration the focus of attention in the user's partially constructed plan, the user's domain knowledge and the user's *receptivity* to the different kinds of rhetorical tools that can be used. This is meant to capture the fact that, for example, some users prefer examples over formal definitions. To construct a definition, their system weights the available predicates with respect to the user's receptivity, and the knowledge base is searched for propositions that can be used to fill the predicate. Each proposition is also evaluated according to its contribution to the dialogue at this point in the discourse, based on the user's plans and knowledge.

7.1.4   Using reasoning about mutual beliefs to plan an utterance

Appelt's generation system, KAMP, embodies a formal representation of the speaker's and hearer's mutual beliefs and uses a formal planning system to plan and produce utterances. KAMP was developed in a task domain where an expert is helping a novice assemble some piece of equipment. One of Appelt's emphases was on producing referring expressions that could be understood by the hearer. KAMP reasons about the knowledge of the speaker and hearer to make sure that, when producing an utterance, the speaker believes it will be understood by the hearer given both their beliefs. Axioms are used to prove that a generation plan formed by KAMP is correct, in that it will satisfy the speaker's goals, which must include being understood by the hearer. KAMP uses knowledge about the goals to be achieved and linguistic rules about English to produce sentences that satisfy multiple goals. KAMP relies on its planning system not only to plan the utterance, but also to generate English.

Although KAMP tailors an utterance according to the hearer's knowledge, the flavor of this work is quite different from TAILOR's. KAMP is very goal-oriented, and utterances are produced to satisfy the speaker's goals. The limited task domain provides a constrained framework for the utterance. The point during the assembly at which the dialog is taking place provides a constraint on the utterance, as there is usually one step to be accomplished at that time. The speaker, or program, need only produce one or two sentences corresponding to the next step in KAMP's plan. In TAILOR, there are no such constraints. Since the generator needs to select facts from the knowledge base to present to the user, the user model provides the framework that delineates a subset of the knowledge base to include in the text.

7.1.5 Dealing with misconceptions about the domain

Another important aspect of user modelling is to detect and correct users' misconceptions about a domain. Kaplan, Mays and McCoy address these issues for different classes of misconceptions and with different emphasis. Kaplan's system, CO-OP, deals with misconceptions that depend on the *content* of the database (Kaplan, 1982), while Mays designed a model aimed at recognizing misconceptions depending on the *structure* of the database (Mays, 1980a). While the thrust of both Kaplan's and Mays' work was in detecting misconceptions, McCoy (1983, 1988, 1989) examined the problem of *correcting* misconceptions. She characterized in a domain independent manner the influences on the choice of additional information to include in answers. She also identified discourse strategies a system can use to produce answers correcting the misconceptions. McCoy's work is similar to ours, as she is concerned with exploiting user models and her generator employs discourse strategies.

Instead of relying on an *a priori* list of possible misconceptions, as do some Computer Aided Instruction systems, e.g., (Stevens *et al.*, 1979; Brown and Burton, 1978; Sleeman, 1982), McCoy classified object related misconceptions based on the knowledge base *feature* they involve. A feature of the knowledge base could be a *superordinate* relation or an *attribute*. Through studies of transcripts, she has identified what types of additional information should be contained in the answer corresponding to each type of object related misconception. A correction schema that dictates what kind of information to include in the answer is associated with each type of misconception. To vary answers depending on the *context* of the misconceptions, McCoy also allows for different "object perspectives." The strategy chosen to correct a misconception is therefore dependent both on the misconception type and the active object perspective.

The work presented in this book differs from this body of work because we are not addressing the issue of detecting and correcting incorrect users' views of the domain, but are interested in providing an answer that is optimally informative given how much the user knows about the domain.

7.1.6 Exploiting the speaker's and hearer's 'pragmatic goals' in generation

Hovy's generation system, PAULINE, incorporates the speaker's interpersonal goals, towards the hearer (such as "being friendly") to produce utterances with both different

159

content and phrasings depending on various pragmatic situations. PAULINE mixes sentence planning and realization, allowing these goals to influence both the content and the phrasing on the sentence (Hovy, 1988a). Unlike TAILOR, PAULINE does not take into consideration the user's domain knowledge in planning an utterance.

7.2 Related work in psychology and reading comprehension

Much research has been conducted in psychology about aspects of man-machine interaction and the distinction between novices and experts. In studying the differences between novices and experts, researchers have mainly looked at the differences in learning style between these two groups, how memory is (re)organized as people acquire knowledge and how one goes from being a novice to becoming an expert. While not directly addressing the issue of how to tailor answers to users having different amounts of domain knowledge, this body of research is of interest as it confirms the validity of the method proposed here.

Of particular interest for this work is a study done by Egan and Gomez (1982, 1988) where they analyzed how individual differences affect difficulty in learning a text editor and showed how the amount of difficulty experienced by users is strongly correlated with user characteristics. Their study suggests that individual differences are very important and should be taken into consideration in designing systems, where it might be appropriate to display information differently depending on the users' characteristics. In particular, a user's level of expertise should be taken into consideration, which is exactly what this work proposes.

More directly connected with user's level of expertise are studies by Chi *et al.* and Lancaster and Kolodner. In a study of categorization and representation of physics problems by experts and novices, Chi and her colleagues found that these two classes of students used very different ways of classifying physics problems (Chi *et al.*, 1981). Experts tended to use abstract physics principles, while novices used the problem's literal features, possibly indicating that novices lacked knowledge about physics principles. In a study in which problem solving capabilities were explored for users with different levels of expertise about the domain, Lancaster and Kolodner found that expert users have more knowledge not only about individual parts of complex devices but also about the causal models involved and the interconnections among parts (Lancaster and Kolodner, 1987). Both these studies suggest that varying only the amount of information might not be enough to tailor an answer to a user's domain knowledge. In this work, another dimension along which to vary an answer is provided, namely the kind of information included in the answer.

Finally, research in reading comprehension emphasizes the importance of previous knowledge in comprehending a text. Davison (1984) criticizes readability formulas, which are strictly based on syntactic structure and choice of vocabulary, claiming they do not adequately measure text difficulty or reading level because they do not measure the background knowledge a text requires in order to be understood. She further argues that the lack of background knowledge is often what makes a text hard to comprehend and shows how readers may fail to understand a text if they do not have required knowledge that is implicitly assumed.

Other researchers have also indicated that readers use their previous knowledge in order to understand new texts (Schank and Abelson, 1977; Anderson *et al.*, 1977). The role of *schemata* (organized knowledge units in memory) in understanding a text and making inferences to complete the meaning of a text is emphasized in (Wilson and Anderson, 1986). In this article summarizing research on the role of prior knowledge in understanding a text, Wilson and Anderson also point out that readers can fail to understand a text mainly because the text assumes knowledge that they do not have.

The results described above suggest that, in order to tailor a text or a response to a user's level of knowledge, it is not enough to simply use different words and grammatical constructions nor to vary only the amount of detail provided in an answer. What the user knows about the domain should play a significant role in deciding what to include in the answer by influencing the kind of information to present to the user. This is exactly what the method proposed in this work does.

7.3 Summary

This chapter presented the related research in generation, user modelling, psychology and reading comprehension. This work draws upon research in generation by using previously defined methods to analyze naturally occurring texts in order to construct discourse strategies (as described in Chapter 3). It is different from previous work on user modelling as it addresses the role of the user's domain knowledge in tailoring an answer, an issue not specifically addressed before. Research in psychology and reading comprehension provides further support for the approach proposed here.

Chapter 8

Beyond TAILOR

In this book, we have shown the feasibility of incorporating a model of a user's knowledge about the domain in a generation system. In this chapter, we first briefly summarize the main points of this work and discuss the feasibility of this approach. Finally, we briefly introduce how our current work goes beyond TAILOR in several directions.

8.1 Main points of this work

In TAILOR, we studied the effect of the user's knowledge about the domain of discourse on the content and organization of a text and showed the feasibility of incorporating a model of the user's domain knowledge in a generation system. Naturally occurring texts show that the user's level of expertise is an important factor to consider when tailoring a text to the user. We thus proposed that a user model containing information about the user's domain knowledge be used in a generation system to guide the decision process.

By analyzing texts, we found that the user's level of expertise affects the *kind* of information to include in a text, as opposed to simply the *amount of detail*. We were thus able to identify more precisely the links between the user model and the generation process. More specifically, the user's level of domain knowledge affects the *choice of a discourse strategy*, and not just the amount of detail to which it is expanded.

In particular, we have described how descriptions of complex physical objects might be tailored to a user's level of expertise. We presented different kinds of knowledge users can have, explaining how a system can take them into consideration in order to

163

generate a description. From our studies of texts, we have found two distinct discourse strategies that are used in describing complex devices. We postulated that the choice of strategy was based on the user's level of expertise. Even though we conducted this study in the domain of complex physical objects, we believe this result can be extended to other domains. (This is briefly discussed below.) We thus proposed that a user model containing information about the user's domain knowledge can be used in a generation system to guide the decision process. We presented the two descriptive strategies that we found showed how they can be mixed to include the appropriate information from the knowledge base, based on the information contained in user model.

Finally we presented TAILOR, a program that generates descriptions tailored to users with various levels of expertise. The user model guides TAILOR in choosing an appropriate discourse strategy at every point in the generation process. TAILOR is also able to automatically mix the strategies to provide device descriptions tailored to users whose domain knowledge fall anywhere along the knowledge spectrum. By representing explicitly the user's domain knowledge in terms of parameters, TAILOR does not require an *a priori* set of stereotypes but can provide a wide variety of descriptions for a whole range of users.

8.2   Feasibility and extensibility of this approach

In this work, we make the assumption that it is desirable for a system to tailor its answer to its users. This is true only provided that this tailoring does not hinder the system's performance or increase its complexity significantly. We argue that tailoring a description to a user's level of expertise using the method described in this work will not add much to the cost of generation and yet provides better answers. Whether a generation system tailors its answers to users or not, it needs a control structure that will guide the decision process both in determining facts to take from the knowledge base and in organizing them, lest the resulting text be incoherent. A discourse strategy is one way to guide its decision process that has been used successfully in previous generation systems. The two discourse strategies used by TAILOR are of comparable complexities to those used in other systems and, in fact, one is essentially identical. Other systems employing discourse strategies must decide which strategy to use to produce a text. The decision is usually based on the question type and the structure and content of the knowledge base. In TAILOR, the user model plays a role, but this does not add any cost to the decision process. Furthermore, to combine the strategies does not add cost either, especially because of the formalism used to represent the strategies. By representing both strategies in the same formalism, here an ATN, the control structure necessary to combine the strategies is readily available. It is not more costly to jump from one node in one network to another node in the same network than to go from one network to another.

TAILOR's user model at this point is coarse grained, in that it contains a list of objects that the user knows and whether he or she understands the basic underlying concepts. A more detailed model might include *exactly* which facts the user knows about objects.

We have shown that a system benefits from a user model that indicates a user's knowledge about the domain, even when the model is not a detailed one. While we feel that a detailed user model would be much harder to obtain, it would be interesting to see whether such a model would allow a system to provide more appropriate answers.

While this work was done only with respect to generating descriptions of complex devices, this approach will be useful in any information seeking environment to which users with different background and knowledge levels have access (this is illustrated in below). Such environment could be a large knowledge base of facts (such as an encyclopedia), a help system, an expert system which needs to communicate with specialists, students and knowledge engineers, or simply with different types of users, such as the expert system for educational diagnosis proposed by (Cohen and Jones, 1989) or the Explainable Expert System (EES) (Neches *et al.*, 1985; Swartout and Smoliar, 1987; Swartout *et al.*, 1991), and tutoring systems (Suthers, 1991). Providing different information in an answer might also be done in explaining the behavior of an expert system which is used both as a teaching tool and as a problem solving engine.

The approach presented in this work would be readily applicable to any domain containing both functional and structural information. In some cases, however, the reverse of what is being done in TAILOR might be necessary: structural information might be more useful for naive and functional information for expert users. Consider, for example, the domain of *organizations*, where there are both constituents and functions. Providing the structure of the organization (e.g., "there is a president, three vice-presidents and five managers") might be sufficient for a relatively naive user, while information on who reports to whom (i.e., functionality) might be more appropriate for a person knowledgable about the organization.

For domains containing different kinds of information, there would be a need to identify which type of information is most appropriate for knowledgeable users and for more naive users. Tailoring to users with different knowledge about the domain by presenting different kinds of information will still be appropriate.

8.3   Current directions

In TAILOR, we studied specifically the effect of the user's level of expertise on the content and organization of the text. As mentioned in Chapter 1, this corresponds to studying one specific aspect of tenor register variation (the user's level of knowledge about the domain) on the content and organization of the text. TAILOR's architecture reflects this concern. The other aspects of register variation were kept constant: TAILOR generates one type of text (descriptions), in one domain (complex physical objects such as telephones and radios), in a non-interactive fashion.

8.3.1 Employing the generator presented here in another domain

We have applied the results of this work in other domains and applications: in particular, we used the basic architecture of TAILOR to build an explanation facility for the Explainable Expert System (EES) (Neches *et al.*, 1985; Swartout and Smoliar, 1987; Swartout *et al.*, 1991). This explanation facility was to satisfy various goals, including being capable of choosing and organizing facts from the knowledge base, of tailoring its texts to the user, and participating in a dialogue with the user and of being adaptive as the dialogue proceeds (Paris, 1991; Moore and Paris, 1991).

Our original goal was to generate definitions of the terms used by the system and the concepts contained in the system's domain model as well as explain the system's reasoning. We were able to use both of the strategies originally used in TAILOR (with an adaptation of the process trace to explain the reasoning of the system, and thus follow different links than those used in TAILOR). Using this generation system, we were also able to tailor these texts to the user's level of expertise, after we identified the appropriateness of the strategies. Using an already existing technique allowed us to start generating texts quickly as well as identify problems with the knowledge base and the design of the expert system.

8.3.2 Building a system with dialogue capabilities

Although we started using the generator presented in this book in its exact form to build an explanation facility for EES, the resulting generation facility did not satisfy all our requirements (Moore and Swartout, 1991; Paris, 1991; Moore and Paris, 1991).[1] In particular, because we used schemata as in TAILOR, the explanation facility could not have *dialogue* and *adaptive* capabilities. As we mentioned above, in TAILOR, we were not concerned with generating text in an interactive fashion – i.e., we were not concerned with having the system participate in a dialogue with the user. For our purposes, then, schemata provided a simple, efficient and elegant solution to the generation planning process.

The interaction mode (the 'one-shot' response) adopted in TAILOR was not sufficient for an expert system generation application, however. Indeed, in naturally occurring advisory interactions (i.e., a person talking to an expert), it has been observed that, at least in expert-novice dialogues, interactions are best viewed as a negotiation process in which the user and expert negotiate the statement of the problem to be solved as well as a solution the user can understand and accept (Pollack *et al.*, 1982; Moore, 1989b; Cawsey, in press). These studies have shown that, in these situations, the 'askers' frequently do not fully understand an expert's response. They often ask follow-up questions, which are requests for clarification, elaboration, or re-explanation of the expert's answer. It is thus important for an explanation facility to be able to provide clarifying texts if an explanation is not understood.

---

[1] The work described in this section was done jointly with Johanna Moore.

In order to handle follow-up questions that may arise in case the user does not fully understand a response given by the system, a generation facility needs to know which part of the text failed to achieve its purpose. Using a schema, the system only knows the top-level discourse that was being achieved by the text (e.g., 'provide a terminology definition'). It does not know what effect the individual parts of the schema are intended to have on the hearer, or how they fit together to achieve the top-level goal. This information has been 'compiled out' into a 'script' that achieves a top-level goal, and the individual steps are no longer explainable. As a result, if the user did not understand a response, the only recovery possible is to use a different strategy to achieve the same top-level discourse goal. It is not possible to re-explain or clarify one part of the schema (Moore and Paris, 1988; Moore and Paris, 1989; Moore and Swartout, 1989; Moore, 1989b; Moore and Swartout, 1991; Paris, 1991; Moore and Paris, 1992a)

To achieve this requirement, a text planner needs not only to have a set of flexible discourse strategies (which is provided by having a set of schemata) but it also needs to 'understand' the text plan it produces. The ability to produce coherent texts that might be tailored is not sufficient. An agent must understand the text it produces in terms of how each part of the text relates to the others, what effect each part is intended to have on the hearer and how the complete text achieves its goal. Once the text has been produced, a text planner must *remember* the discourse goals being achieved at any point (or its *intentions* in generating text) and which rhetorical structures were being used (i.e., the system must be able to recognize the links between discourse goals and rhetorical structures). Otherwise, recovering from communication failure and learning (or self-tuning) is not possible. There is thus a need for an explicit *text plan*, which records how the text was constructed and why. This text plan must contain a *specification of the intended effect of individual parts of the text on the hearer and how the parts relate to one another*. The schemata employed in our initial attempt lacked such a specification (as it had been 'compiled out'), rendering our interactive requirement impossible to fulfill. We thus had to look for other ways to represent discourse strategies.

Schemata were not the only generation techniques that could have been employed: Appelt's system generated text by explicitly reasoning about the effects of surface speech acts on the hearer's beliefs (Appelt, 1985). This approach is based on a formal axiomatization of illocutionary actions which may be used to reason about the beliefs of the hearer and speaker and the effects of surface speech acts on these beliefs (Cohen and Perrault, 1979; Cohen and Levesque, 1990). Systems using this approach so far only plan short (one- or two-sentence) texts to achieve speakers' goal(s). While it is assumed by this approach that appropriate axioms can be added to generate longer (multi-sentential) texts, this has not been demonstrated, and we believe that building a system to produce multi-sentential texts directly from the logics proposed by proponents of this approach would prove to be computationally infeasible. We thus found the need to link intentional goals and rhetorical devices (Moore and Paris, 1989; Moore and Paris, 1992b).

Others have tried to make the connection between rhetorical relations and speaker's intentions. As we have mentioned earlier in this book, Hobbs (1978, 1979, 1985) characterizes coherence in terms of a set of binary *coherence relations* between a current utterance and the preceding discourse. He identified four reasons why a speaker breaks a discourse into more than one clause and classified the relations accordingly. For example, if a speaker needs to connect new information with what is already known by the hearer, the speaker chooses one of the *linkage relations*, such as *background* or *explanation*. Although Hobbs provides definitions for these relations, the speaker's intentions are not an explicit part of the formal definition of the relation, making it harder to link discourse goals and rhetorical structure.

In an attempt to define a theory of coherence, Mann and Thompson also specified a set of rhetorical relations.[2] Their definition of each relation indicates constraints on the two entities being related (the nucleus and the satellite) as well as constraints on their combination, *and a specification of the effect which the speaker is attempting to achieve on the hearer's beliefs or inclinations.* Thus RST provides an explicit connection between the speaker's intentions and the rhetorical means used to achieve those intentions and could be used as a basis for a text generation system after a more precise formulation of the constraints. We have argued in Chapter 3 that we could not use RST in a straightforward way in a generation system as the specification of the relation did not provide enough constraints as to what to say next. In order to use RST, a text generation system must have control strategies that dictate how to find such knowledge in the knowledge base, when and what relations should occur, how many times, and in what order.

One attempt at formalization was made by Hovy (1988), who operationalized a subset of the RST relation definitions for use as plan operators in a *text structuring process.* Hovy's structurer employs a top-down planning mechanism to order a *given* set of input elements into a coherent text. He adapted RST for the text structuring task by encoding the specification of the intended effect of an RST relation as the goal that the plan operator can be used to achieve, and the constraints on relations as the subgoals that must be satisfied. In this system, then, rhetorical relations are used explicitly, but the *discourse goals* or *intentions* that these relations achieve is not separately represented.

However, in our efforts to use RST to construct a text plan that includes both the intentions of individual segments of the text and an indication of the rhetorical relations between segments, we found such an operationalization to be inadequate in the general case, because, in general, the mapping between intentions and rhetorical relations is *not* a one-to-one mapping. That is, a single intention may be achieved by a variety of different rhetorical relations, and a rhetorical means can be used to achieve various intentional goal. For example, if the system's intention is to make the hearer identify a specific object, it could provide its *purpose*, using a *purpose* RST relation, its *color*, using a *elaboration-object-attribute* RST relation, or its *location*, a *circumstance* relation. If a system only records the rhetorical means used, it has no way of recovering the intention (Moore and Paris, 1989; Moore and Paris, 1992b). As a result, a system like Hovy's that only reasons and records the rhetorical relations necessary to plan a text

---

[2]Hobbs' coherence relations and Mann and Thompson's Rhetorical Structure Theory (RST) were already discussed in Chapter 3.

suffers from the same problem as schemata: it cannot participate in a dialogue, as the intentional structure of the text that is necessary to recover from communication failure and answer a follow-up questions is lost.

We thus found that the other current generation techniques also had shortcomings for our purpose of generating multi-sentential texts and participating in a dialogue.[3] We therefore had the need to develop a new planner that would incorporate both the discourse goals being achieved at any point and how the pieces of text relate to one another. This new text planner constructs explanations based on the intentions of the speaker at each step and notes the rhetorical relations that hold between text spans. It records all of its decisions in an *explicit text plan*. By recording this planning process, the system is able to reason about its previous utterances both to interpret and answer users' follow-up questions (Moore, 1989a; Moore and Swartout, 1989; Moore, 1989b).

In our new system, intentional and rhetorical knowledge are explicitly represented. Discourse strategies are represented in terms of small plans. A planning mechanism reasons about the discourse goals to be achieved and the rhetorical means needed to achieve them to construct a text. In this new system, plans achieve two types of goals: *communicative goals*, which represent intentions of the speaker, and *linguistic goals*, which correspond to the linguistic means available to speakers for achieving their communicative goals. Associated with each plan is a list of constraints, that is a list of conditions that must be true before the plan can be applied. Constraints may refer to facts in the system's knowledge bases, information in the user model, information in the dialogue history, or information about the evolving text plan. Using the results of the work described in this book, this new generation system also uses the user model (in this case both the user's level of expertise and user's goals) to guide its decision process (Moore and Paris, 1992a). As in TAILOR's domain, we found that the user's level of expertise affected the type of text that needed to be generated. This is reflected in the user model constraint associated with each plan. We therefore see that, although we now use an entirely different architecture (reflecting our different needs), the theoretical results of our earlier work are readily applicable in this new application and new domain.

8.3.3 Tailoring the phrasing of a text

In TAILOR, we were mainly concerned with tailoring the content and organization of a text. As we mentioned in Chapter 1, this tailoring should occur at all levels of linguistic realization, from the content and organization of the text as a whole to lexical and syntactic constructions of individual sentences (i.e., the *phrasing* of the text). In this book, we have already given examples of text in which both the content and the organization varied depending on the user's level of expertise, and we have shown how a generation system can tailor text to the user. Tailoring the content and the

---

[3]We only briefly summarize the reasons here. The interested reader is referred to the references given for further details.

organization of a text is not sufficient, however: It is important that the *phrasing* of a text be also tailored to the hearer – otherwise it may be just as ineffective as texts which wrongly direct attention or which rely on knowledge that the hearer does not have (Bateman and Paris, 1989; Bateman and Paris, 1991). Indeed, people speak differently according to the situation, even when they talk about the same thing, as was illustrated already in Figure 1.1, Chapter 1.

We have now started to address this issue, still within the EES explanation facility, in order to eventually develop a framework within which tailoring to the situation can occur at *all* levels of linguistic realization.[4] In that work, we adopt more strictly *register theory* (Halliday, 1978) from Systemic Linguistics (Halliday, 1973) as the theoretical background for our research, because of the methodology it provides, as well as the extensive body of work already performed on this issue (Cloran, 1987; Gregory, 1967; Hasan, 1978; Hasan, 1984; Hasan, 1989; Mackay and Mountford, 1978; Martin and Rothery, 1981; Ure, 1969; Ure and Ellis, 1969; White, 1974). As already mentioned, the different kinds of language called for in varying situations are called *registers*. Registers may be seen as describing the 'argots' used by different classes of users. The general aim of the theory is to make *explicit* the links between situational features and linguistic features and thus specify the linguistic consequences of using language in particular situations. In our current work, we wish to provide a framework within which it is possible to gain *systematic* control over phrasing. This framework will allow the expression of the properties of a situation that define the kind of language the situation calls for as well as the explicit representation of the links these situational properties and the lexico-grammatical resources of a generation system, thus ensuring that the phrasing of an automatically generated text is appropriately tailored according to the situation.

In a pilot study that involved generating explanations for an expert system tailored to three types of users (Bateman and Paris, 1989), we showed that it is possible to specify the type of language required in a given situation and to build a text planning system that uses that specification to vary the phrasing of its text. In that study, we restricted our attention to a few kinds of texts in the domain of digital circuit diagnosis. We analyzed these texts and the situations in which they appeared. Based on our analysis, we constructed specifications of the important features of the situation, and of the linguistic variations among the texts. The situational features were then used as an additional source of input to the text generation process. They controlled the grammar, thus controlling linguistic variation.

In our pilot study, we examined the different forms of language that would be required for the expert system to interact with the three different types of user types: system developers (users who want to make sure that the knowledge base is correctly represented and that the system is working properly), end-users (users who want to follow the system's reasoning, but do not know much about expert system technology – or even about computer science), and students using a system as a tutoring aid and who are novice with respect to the application domain and to computer science. We found two distinct kinds of linguistic variation: the *head-modified structure* of a sentence, and the

---

[4]This is joint work with John Bateman.

The system is faulty, if there exists a O in the set of the output terminals of the system such that the expected value of the signal part of O does not equal the actual value of the signal part of O and for all I in the set of the input terminals of the system, the expected value of the signal part of I equals the actual value of the signal part of I.

Text generated for system developers

The system is faulty, if all of the expected values of its input terminals equal their actual values and the expected value of one of its output terminals does not equal its actual value.

Text generated for end-users

The system is faulty, if its inputs are fine and its output is wrong.

Text generated for students

Figure 8.1: Examples of variations generated from the same propositional input for different user types

grammatical realization of a proposition. We implemented the mechanisms necessary to control the generation process to produce these variations, given a specification of the user types. Some examples of texts generated during the pilot study are shown in Figure 8.1. These three texts are generated from the same underlying representation and they are all appropriate responses to the question: 'What is a faulty system?' in the digital circuit diagnosis context. However, they are differentiated according to the type of user involved.

The set of situational features used in this initial study was very restricted, however. Based again on text analysis, we are now extending our set of situational features to develop a language that can be used to specify the general characteristics of situations that have an influence on linguistic realization. Importantly, we also want to capture generalizations across more or less similar situations. We seek to define registers in terms of selections of situational features that call for the selection of particular corresponding linguistic features. To capture generalizations across more or less similar situations, we aim at organizing the situational features that define registers into a *network of interdependent choices*, i.e., a *register network*, each of which may constrain the linguistic alternatives available in the grammar by requiring specified sets of linguistic features to occur. This organization is already the one chosen for the grammar (Mann, 1983). The results of making particular situational 'settings' or choices in the register network would then have the effect of preselecting (or of limiting) alternatives of expression in the grammar network. This would give rise to

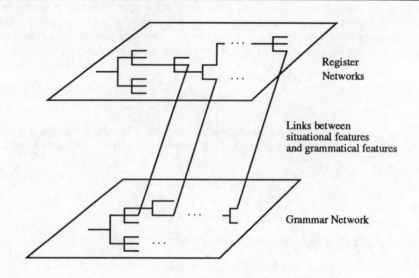

Figure 8.2: Architecture for controlling phrasing

the architecture shown in Figure 8.2 (also used in (Patten, 1988)).

Finally, we are also developing further the mechanisms necessary to gain control over fine-level grammatical details, as well as designing a methodology by which the systematic relationship between situations and realization can be found, represented, and used to tailor generated texts for any new domain.

8.3.4 Bringing the whole generation process under register control

Once a framework to systematically tailor the phrasing of a text to the situation at hand and a register network have been developed, we will attempt to provide a uniform architecture in which language can be tailored to the situation at all levels of the linguistic realization: that is, the choice of discourse strategy will also depend on the register features chosen. In the beginning, this corresponds to re-implementing TAILOR in a different architecture: instead of a procedure as now used in TAILOR to choose the appropriate discourse strategy, the situation features which affect the choice would be represented as register features, with a link to the appropriate discourse strategy. Furthermore, we would also study the conditions which affect some of the decisions currently set by hand in the form of various parameters, such as the number of side links necessary to include in the description, the generation of long *vs* short descriptions, or the ranking of the links. These would also be represented as register features which would affect how the planning is done. Importantly, these parameters need to be set differently depending on the situation (as already pointed out in, e.g., pages 60, 70, and 74). By controlling the generation process at the register level, we would avoid having to re-set these parameters by hand for each situation, and, the link between situation and text would be more systematic.

TAILOR only had two strategies, which were clearly differentiated in their use by the content of the user model. Re-implementing TAILOR to bring the discourse strategies under register control is thus a relatively simple task. A general generation system, however, will need to have a library of discourse strategies. Already, in the explanation facility we developed for EES, we have extended the number of strategies available to the system and continue to do so (Mittal and Paris, 1990; Mittal and Paris, 1992). As we mentioned earlier, the strategies now make use of both the discourse goals that a speaker might have and the rhetorical strategies that are available to achieve these goals. In their constraints, the strategies indicate in which situation they are applicable. As the plan library grows and the system must generate texts for an ever-increasing number of domains and situations, the same information (e.g., requirements of use and other preconditions) sometimes has to be represented several times, and it becomes harder to identify the relationships among various plans as well as add more plans and modify existing plans because of their interrelationships. For example, the strategy to achieve a specific discourse goal might be slightly different depending on the user type. We currently would need to write two plans with two different constraints on the user model. In order to ultimately incorporate our generator in the unified architecture we envisioned, we need to be able to specify more clearly the links between the user types (and other register features) and the discourse strategies. As a first step, we are now trying to identify precisely the different knowledge sources that are necessary to generate coherent discourse (including communicative goals, text types, schemas, discourse structure relations, and theme development patterns), and represent these (and their relationships) distinctly and declaratively, with a clear separation of the declarative and procedural knowledge required in a generation system (Paris and Maier, 1991; Hovy *et al.*, 1992). This will allow us to then represent more explicitly the links between the situation and the generation process at the content and organization level.

8.3.5 Providing a system with adaptive capabilities

Finally, we are looking into the possibility for the system to be able to reason about its behavior over a period of time (one or more dialogues) in order to improve its communication abilities (Paris, 1991). We postulate that, when there is a communication failure and it becomes clear that the strategy adopted is not the right one for the user, the speaker has several options: initially, he or she can simply change its model of the user and change its choice of strategy appropriately. If this type of communication failure occurs frequently, the speaker might decide that its user model recognition process is at fault and attempt to tune it. Following this model, the links between the user model and the discourse strategies (or plans) would remain unchanged. If communication failures of the type mentioned above still occur, the speaker might decide to change its links between the user model and the strategies: this corresponds to realizing that a specific discourse strategy, although initially thought to be adequate for a particular user type, is found to be inappropriate for this type. The speaker must then either change its links or add new links (and create new strategies, possibly by modifying existing ones). We are investigating the plausibility of these hypothesis[5] and would like to design mechanisms to allow our text generation system to behave in a similar way.

This is desirable as a generation facility for a large system to be used by many users is unlikely to have a complete and correct library of discourse strategies, know exactly how to judge a user and have the correct links between user model and strategies. Indeed, it is very hard to foresee every situation that might occur and get transcripts of the exact type of interactions that will be taking place between the system and the users. It is thus desirable for a system to be able to perform this type of adaptive behavior. Furthermore, as people interact, they change their discourse strategies to reflect the feedback they obtained on their utterances. Likewise, a generation system should be able to learn from experience and respond to feedback from the users by modifying its existing strategies. It is important to note that this task will be facilitated when we have developed a framework in which the knowledge sources for generation are explicitly and separately represented and in which the links between the situation and the generation resources are clearly and explicitly described.

---

[5]The empirical work is being conducted in collaboration with Béatrice Cahour.

Appendix A

More examples of the texts studied:

Texts from high school text books,

junior encyclopedia and the manual for novices

A Telegraph Sounder (Blackwood *et al.*, 1951)

By pressing the key, you close the electric circuit. Then, the electromagnet pulls down the iron plate, mounted on the pivoted bar.

An Electric Bell (Blackwood *et al.*, 1951)

The current magnetizes the U-magnet, which pulls over the iron plate and makes the clapper strike the bell. Then the circuit is cut at the contact breaker, the magnet releases the iron plate, and a spring pulls it back.

A Simple Telephone (Blackwood *et al.*, 1951)

By speaking into the mouthpiece you make the transmitter diaphragm vibrate and thus vary the pressure on the carbon grains. This varies their resistance, so that the current varies. The strength of the electomagnet varies, pulling the receiver diaphragm to and fro. It reproduces the sound.

A Model Commutator (Blackwood *et al.*, 1951)

As it rotates, each half ring is first negative, then positive. The current through the wire loop reverses twice for each revolution.

Thermometers (Reichlis and Lemon, 1952)

In a metallic thermometer – or a dial type – heat expansion causes a coiled compound bar to twist. The twisting bar turns a pointer to indicate the correct temperature on a dial, which is calibrated (that is, properly marked off).

Cathode Ray Tube (Verwiebe *et al.*, 1962)

This tube is highly evacuated. When a cathode ray (stream of electrons) leaves the cathode (negative electrode) and strikes the metal plate *A*, most of the electrons are stopped. Only those electrons passing through the slit will fall on plate *B*. Plate *B* is coated with a fluorescent material, and as the electrons strike plate *B*, a fluorescent light appears. When a magnet is brought near the tube, the electron beam is deflected just as a wire carrying a current near a magnet would be deflected. Both the beam and the wire are deflected in the direction indicated by the right-hand rule given for motors.

The Electron Microscope (Baker *et al.*, 1957)

Electrons are deflected by either electric or magnetic fields, and a stream of them can be focused by a suitable field of either kind just as light is focused by a lens.

Galvanometer (Britannica-Junior, 1963)

A galvanometer is an instrument for measuring an amount of current. If two magnets are brought together, they try to arrange themselves with their magnetic field lined up in the same direction. All galvanometers make use of this principle. In one type of galvanometer a coil of wire hangs between the poles of one or more permanent horseshoe magnets. The electromagnetic field is set up by a flow of electricity. The coil rotates (turns) to line up with the field of the permanent magnet. The stronger the current, the more the coil will turn. A mirror fastened to the wires reflects a small beam of light from a lamp onto a dial scale as the coil is twisted. Some galvanometers may read directly from a pointer on the scale. Another group of galvanometers uses a fixed coil of wire with a permanent magnet turned inside the coil. A pointer attached to the magnet shows the amount of rotation, in other words, the strength of the current.

Automobile Engine (Weissler and Weissler, 1973)

An automobile engine produces power by burning a mixture of gasoline and air in a small space called a combustion chamber. When the mixture burns, it expands and pushes out in direction. The combustion chamber is often located just above a cylinder, into which is installed a closely fitting plug called a piston. The piston is capable of being moved up and down in the cylinder. When the piston is lowered in a running engine, it creates a vacuum in the cylinder and draws in a mixture of fuel and air. The piston is then pushed up to the top of the cylinder, compressing the air-fuel charge. A spark ignites the mixture, which expands and pushed the piston downward.

Appendix B

More examples of the texts studied:
Texts from adult encyclopedias
and the manual for experts

Galvanometer (Collier, 1962)

The commonest type of galvanometer is the moving-coil galvanometer. A permanent magnet creates a magnetic field in the air gap. The coil is supported by the suspension wire in such a manner that the coil can rotate in the air gap without touching any part of the magnet.

Galvanometer (Collier, 1962)

A galvanometer of the D'Arsonval type is used to measure the magnitude of electric current. It consists of a needle attached to a coil suspended between the poles of a horseshoe magnet.

Telescope – Summary (Britannica, 1964)

Instrument for viewing or detecting distant and particularly extra-terrestrial objects, including optical telescopes, which combines lenses or mirrors or both to form a visible image, and radio telescopes which pick up and analyze radio-frequency electromagnet radiations.

General Description of the Engine (Chevrolet, 1978)

Starting at the front of the engine, cylinders in the left bank are numbered 1-3-5 and cylinders in the right bank are numbered 2-4-6.

The crankshaft, nodular cast-iron, is supported in the crankcase by four bearing. The number two bearing is the end thrust bearing.

The crankshaft is counterbalanced by weights cast integral with the crankshaft. Additional counterbalancing is obtained from a flex plate and harmonic balancer.

The tin plated alloy pistons have full skirts and are cam ground. Two transverse slots in the oil ring grooves extend through the piston wall and permit drain back of oil collected by the oil ring.

The camshaft is supported in the crankcase by five steel-backed babbitt-lined bearing. It is driven from the crankshafts by sprockets and chain.

The cylinder heads are cast-iron and incorporate integral valve stem guides and rocker arm shaft pedestral. Right and left cylinder heads are identical and interchangeable, although in service, it is good practice to reinstall the cylinder heads on the side from which they are removed.

The intake utilizes a low restriction, dual intake manifold. It is bolted to the inner edges of both cylinder heads so that hat it connects with all inlet ports. Since the intake manifold is cast-iron, as is the carburetor throttle body, the manifold incorporates a special exhaust heat passage to warm the throttle body...

Electric Motors (Britannica, 1964)

Motors must consists of two parts - a rotor and stator. The rotor is usually round and in the moving portion. It contains conductors to establish and shape magnetic fields that will interact with other magnetic fields produced by the stator. The rotor also may have a contacting device (slip rings or commutator) to connect it electrically with the external circuit, together with a support shaft and bearings, an integral blower for cooling, etc. The stator consists of similar magnetic materials and electrical conductors to establish and shape the magnetic fields, as well as the frame to support the whole machine. The manner in which the conductors are arranged (and in which the magnetic fields are controlled) determines the type of motor and its characteristics.

Vacuum-tube Voltmeter (Collier, 1962)

The vacuum-tube voltmeter employs an electron tube as a rectifier. In one form of vacuum-tube voltmeter, the two halves of a duplex diode rectifier tube are sued, one half rectifying during one half of the cycle of the voltage being measured and the other rectifying during the other half of the cycle.

Bibliography

(Allen and Perrault, 1980) J. F. Allen and C. R. Perrault. Analyzing Intention in Utterances. *Artificial Intelligence*, 15(1):143–178, 1980.

(Allen, 1990) James F. Allen. User Models: Theory, Method, and Practice. *International Journal of Man-Machine Studies*, 32:511–543, 1990.

(Anderson *et al.*, 1977) R. C. Anderson, R. J. Spiro, and M. C. Anderson. Schemata as Scaffolding for the Representation of Information in Connected Discourse. Technical Report 24, Center for the Study of Reading, Urbana, Illinois, 1977.

(Appelt, 1985) Douglas E. Appelt. *Planning English Sentences*. Cambridge University Press, Cambridge, England, 1985.

(Arens and Hovy, 1990) Yigal Arens and Eduard Hovy. How to Describe What? Towards a Theory of Modality Utilization. In *Proceedings of the Twelfth Annual Conference of the Cognitive Science Society*, 1990.

(Baker and Danyluk, 1986) Michelle Baker and Andrea P. Danyluk. Representing Physical Devices. Technical report, Columbia University Department of Computer Science, 1986.

(Baker *et al.*, 1957) D. L. Baker, R. B. Brownlee, and Fuller R. W. *Elements of Physics*. Allyn and Bacon, Inc., Newton, Massachusetts, 1957.

(Ballim and Wilks, 1991) Afzal Ballim and Yorick Wilks. Beliefs, stereotypes and dynamic agent modeling. *User Modeling and User-Adapted Interaction*, 1(1):33–65, 1991.

(Bateman and Paris, 1989) John A. Bateman and Cécile L. Paris. Phrasing a Text in Terms the User Can Understand. In *Proceedings of the Eleventh International Joint Conference on Artificial Intelligence*, pages 1511–1517, Detroit, Michigan, August 20–25 1989.

(Bateman and Paris, 1991) John A. Bateman and Cécile L. Paris. Constraining the Deployment of Lexicogrammatical Resources During Text Generation: Towards a Computational Instantiation of Register Theory. In Eija Ventola, editor, *Functional and Systemic Linguistics: Approaches and Uses*, chapter 5, pages 81–106. Mouton de Gruyter, Berlin, New York, 1991.

(Biber, 1988) Douglas Biber. *Variation across speech and writing*. Cambridge University Press, Cambridge, England, 1988.

(Biber, 1989) Douglas Biber. A typology of English Texts. *Linguistics*, 27:3–43, 1989.

(Binot *et al.*, 1990) J.L. Binot, P. Falzon, R. Perez, B. Peroche, N. Sheehy, J. Rouault, and M. Wilson. Architecture of a multimodal dialogue interface for knowledge-based systems. In *Proceedings of the ESPRIT 90 conference*, Boston, 1990. Kluwer Academic Publishers.

(Blackwood *et al.*, 1951) O.H. Blackwood, W.B. Herron, and W.C. Kelly. *The High School Physics*. Ginn and Company, 1951.

(Britannica-Junior, 1963) *Britannica Junior Encyclopedia*, Chicago, Illinois., 1963. Encyclopaedia Britannica, Inc.

(Britannica, 1964) *The New Encyclopedia Britannica*, 1964. Encyclopedia Britannica Inc.

(Brown and Burton, 1978) J. S. Brown and R. R. Burton. Diagnostics models for procedural bugs in basic mathematical skills. *Cognitive Science*, 2(2):155–192, 1978.

(Brown and Yule, 1983) G. Brown and G. Yule. *Discourse Analysis*. Cambridge University Press, Cambridge, England, 1983.

(Bunt, 1990) H. C. Bunt. Modular Incremental Modelling of Belief and Intention. In *Proceedings of the Second International Workshop on User Modeling*. AAAI and the University of Hawaii, 1990.

(Cahour and Paris, 1991) Béatrice Cahour and Cécile L. Paris. Role and Use of User Models. in the *Proceedings of the IJCAI-91 Workshop on Agent Modelling for Intelligent Interaction*, August 1991. Sydney, Australia.

(Calistri-Yeh, 1991) Randall J. Calistri-Yeh. Utilizing user models to handle ambiguity and misconceptions in robust plan recognition. *User Modeling and User-Adapted Interaction*, 1(4):289–322, 1991.

(Carberry, 1983) Sandra Carberry. Tracking User Goals in an Information-Seeking Environment. In *Proceedings of the Third National Conference on Artificial Intelligence*, pages 59–63, Washington, D.C., August 22–26 1983.

(Carberry, 1988) Sandra Carberry. Plan Recognition and User Modeling. *Computational Linguistics*, 14 (3), September 1988.

(Carberry, 1990) Sandra Carberry. *Plan Recognition in Natural Language Dialogue*. MIT Press, Cambridge, Massachusetts, 1990.

(Carbonell, 1970) J. R. Carbonell. AI in CAI: An Artificial Intelligence Approach to Computer-Aided Instruction. *IEEE Transactions on Man-Machine Systems*, 11:190–202, 1970.

(Carenini and Moore, 1993) Giuseppe Carenini and Johanna D. Moore. Generating explanations in context. In *Proceedings of the International Workshop on Intelligent User Interfaces*, Orlando, Florida, January 1993.

(Carr and Goldstein, 1977) B. Carr and I. Goldstein. Overlays: A Theory of Modeling for Computer Aided Instruction. Memo 406, Massachusetts Institute of Technology, Artificial Intelligence Laboratory, February 1977.

(Cawsey, in press) Alison Cawsey. Planning Interactive Explanations. *International Journal of Man-Machine Studies*, in press.

(Chappel and Cahour, 1991) Helen Chappel and Béatrice Cahour. User Modeling for Multi-Modal Co-Operative Dialogue with KBS. Deliverable D3, Esprit Project P2474, 1991.

(Chemical, 1978) *The Kirk-Othmer Encyclopedia of Chemical Technology*, New York, 1978. John Wiley & Sons.

(Chevrolet, 1978) Chevrolet. *Chevrolet Service Manual*. Detroit, Michigan, 1978. General Motors Corporation.

(Chi *et al.*, 1981) M.T.H. Chi, R. Glaser, and E. Rees. Expertise in Problem Solving. In R. J. Sternberg, editor, *Advances in the Psychology of Human Intelligence*, volume 1. Lawrence Erlbaum, Hillsdale, 1981.

(Chin, 1986) David N. Chin. User Modelling in UC, the UNIX Consultant. In *Proceedings of the 1986 Conference on Human Factors in Computing Systems*, 1986.

(Chin, 1989) David N. Chin. KNOME: Modeling What the User Knows in UC. In Alfred Kobsa and Wolfgang Wahlster, editors, *User Models in Dialog Systems*, pages 74–107. Springer-Verlag, Symbolic Computation Series, Berlin, 1989.

(Cloran, 1987) Carmel Cloran. Negotiating new contexts in conversation. *Occasional Papers in Systemic Linguistics*, 1:85–110, 1987.

(Cohen and Jones, 1989) Robin Cohen and Marlene Jones. Incorporating User Models into Expert Systems for Educational Diagnosis. In Alfred Kobsa and Wolfgang Wahlster, editors, *User Models in Dialog Systems*, pages 35–51. Springer-Verlag, Symbolic Computation Series, Berlin, 1989.

(Cohen and Levesque, 1990) Philip R. Cohen and Hector Levesque. Rational Interaction as the Basis for Communication. In Philip R. Cohen, Jerry Morgan, and Martha E. Pollack, editors, *Intentions in Communication*. MIT Press, Cambridge, Massachusetts, 1990.

(Cohen and Perrault, 1979) Philip R. Cohen and C. Raymond Perrault. Elements of a Plan-Based Theory of Speech Acts. *Cognitive Science*, 3:177–212, 1979.

(Cohen *et al.*, 1991) Robin Cohen, Fei Song, Bruce Spencer, and Peter van Beek. Exploiting temporal and novel information from the user in plan recognition. *User Modeling and User-Adapted Interaction*, 1(2):125–148, 1991.

(Collier, 1962) *Collier's Encyclopedia*, New York, 1962. The Crowell-Collier Publishing Company 1962; William Halsey, editorial director.

(Cullingford *et al.*, 1982) R. E. Cullingford, M. W. Krueger, M. Selfridge, and M. A. Bienkowski. Automated construction of classifications: Conceptual clustering versus numerical taxonomy. *IEEE Transactions on Systems, Man and Cybernetics*, 12(2):168–181, 1982.

(Danlos, 1987) Laurence Danlos. *The linguistic basis of text generation*. Cambridge University Press, Cambridge, 1987.

(Davey, 1978) A. Davey. *Discourse Production: A Computer Model of Some Aspects of a Speaker*. Edinburgh University Press, Edinburgh, 1978. Published version of Ph.D. dissertation, University of Edinburgh, 1974.

(Davison, 1984) A. Davison. Readability Formulas and Comprehension. In Laura R. Roehler Gerald G. Duffy and Jana Mason, editors, *Comprehension Instruction; Perspectives and Suggestions*. Longman, New York, London, 1984.

(Egan and Gomez, 1982) D. E. Egan and L. M. Gomez. Characteristics of people who can learn to use computer text editors: Hints for future text editor design and training. In *Proceedings of the ASIS Annual Meeting*, volume 19, 1982.

(Egan and Gomez, 1983) D. E. Egan and L. M. Gomez. Assaying, isolating and accomodating individual differences in learning a complex skill. In Dillon R. F., editor, *Individual Differences In Cognition*, volume 2. Academic Press, New York, 1983.

(Elhadad *et al.*, 1991) Michael Elhadad, Steve Feiner, Kathleen McKeown, and Doree Seligmann. Generating Customized Text and Graphics in the COMET Explanation Testbed. In *Proceedings 1991 Winter Simulation Conference*, pages 1058–1065, Phoenix, Arizona, December 8–11 1991.

(Elhadad, 1991) Michael Elhadad. FUF: The Universal Unifier User Manual Version 5.0. Technical Report CUCS-038-91, Columbia University, New York, 1991.

(Elhadad, 1992) Michael Elhadad. *Using Argumentation to Control Lexical Choice: A Functional Unification Implementation*. PhD thesis, Columbia University, New York, August 1992.

(Eller and Carberry, 1991) Rhonda Eller and Sandra Carberry. A meta-rule approach to flexible plan recognition in dialogue. *User Modeling and User-Adapted Interaction*, 2(1–2):27–53, 1991.

(Encyclopedia of Science, 1982) *The New Encyclopedia of Science*, Milwaukee, Wisconsin, 1982. Raintree Publishers.

(Falzon, 1990) Pierre Falzon. Human-Computer Interaction: Lessons From Human-Human Communication. In Pierre Falzon, editor, *Cognitive Ergonomics: Understanding, Learning and Designing Human-Computer Interaction*, pages 51–67. Academic Press, London, England, 1990.

(Feiner and McKeown, 1990) Steve Feiner and Kathleen McKeown. Coordinating Text and Graphics in Explanation Generation. In *Proceedings of the Eighth National Conference on Artificial Intelligence*, pages 442–449, Boston, Massachusetts, July 29–August 3 1990.

(Feiner and McKeown, 1991) Steve Feiner and Kathleen McKeown. Automating the Generation of Coordinated Multimedia Explanations. *IEEE Computer*, 24(10):33–41, October 1991.

(Feiner *et al.*, 1991) Steve Feiner, Diane Litman, Kathleen McKeown, and Rebecca Passonneau. Towards Coordinated Temporal Multimedia Presentations. In *Proceedings of the AAAI-91 Workshop Workshop on Intelligent Multimedia Interfaces*, pages 4–8, Anaheim, California, July 15 1991.

(Feiner, 1988) Steve Feiner. An Architecture for Knowledge-Based Graphical Interfaces. In *Proceedings of the ACM/SIGCHI Workshop on Architectures for Intelligent Interfaces: Elements and Prototypes*, pages 59–62, Monterey, California, 1988.

(Fikes and Nilsson, 1971) Richard E. Fikes and Nils J. Nilsson. STRIPS: A New Approach to the Application of Theorem Proving to Problem Solving. *Artificial Intelligence*, 2:189–208, 1971.

(Goldman, 1974) Neil Goldman. *Computer Generation of Natural Language from a Deep Conceptual Information Processing*. PhD thesis, Department of Computer Science, Yale University, Connecticut, 1974.

(Goldman, 1975) Neil Goldman. Conceptual generation. In R. C. Schank, editor, *Conceptual Information Processing*. North-Holland Publishing Co, Amsterdam, 1975.

(Goodman and Litman, 1992) Bradley A. Goodman and Diane J. Litman. On the interaction between plan recognition and intelligent interfaces. *User Modeling and User-Adapted Interaction*, 2(1–2):55–82, 1992.

(Gregory, 1967) Michael Gregory. Aspects of varieties differentiation. *Journal of Linguistics*, 3:177–198, 1967.

(Grice, 1969) H. P. Grice. Utterer's meaning and intentions. *Philosophical Review*, 68(2):147–177, 1969.

(Grice, 1975) H. P. Grice. Logic and Conversation. In P. Cole and J. L. Morgan, editors, *Syntax and Semantics III: Speech Acts*, pages 41–58. Academic Press, New York, 1975.

(Grimes, 1975) J. E Grimes. *The Thread of Discourse*. Mouton, The Hague, 1975.

(Halliday, 1973) Michael A.K. Halliday. *Explorations in the Functions of Language*. Edward Arnold, London, 1973.

(Halliday, 1978) Michael A. K. Halliday. *Language as social semiotic*. Edward Arnold, London, 1978.

(Hasan, 1978) Ruqaiya Hasan. Text in the Systemic-Functional Model. In Wolfgang Dressler, editor, *Current Trends in Text Linguistics*, pages 228–246. Mouton de Gruyter, Berlin, New York, 1978.

(Hasan, 1979) Rukaya Hasan. On the Notion of Text. In J. Petoefi, editor, *Text vs. Sentence (Papers in Text Linguistics, volume 20)*. Helmut Buske Verlag, Hamburg, 1979.

(Hasan, 1984) Ruqaiya Hasan. What kind of resource is language? *Australian Review of Applied Linguistics*, 7, 1984.

(Hasan, 1989) Ruqaiya Hasan. The representation of meaning in the systemic functional model. Technical report, Department of Linguistics, Macquarie University, Sydney, Australia, 1989. Paper presented at the 16th. International Systemic Congress, Helsinki, Finland.

(Hayes and Reddy, 1979) P. Hayes and R. Reddy. Graceful Interaction in Man-Machine Communication. In *Proceedings of the Sixth International Joint Conference on Artificial Intelligence*, Tokyo, August 1979.

(Hobbs and Robinson, 1978) J. R. Hobbs and J. J. Robinson. Why Ask? Technical Note 169, SRI International, October 1978.

(Hobbs, 1978) Jerry R. Hobbs. Why is Discourse Coherent? Technical Report 176, SRI International, Menlo Park, California, November 1978.

(Hobbs, 1979) Jerry R. Hobbs. Coherence and Coreference. *Cognitive Science*, 3(1):67–90, 1979.

(Hobbs, 1985) Jerry R. Hobbs. On the Coherence and Structure of Discourse. Technical Report CSLI–85–37, Center for the Study of Language and Information, Stanford University, Stanford, California, October 1985.

(Hoeppner et al., 1984) W. Hoeppner, K. Morik, and H. Marburger. Talking it Over: The Natural Dialog System HAM-ANS. Technical Report ANS–26, Research Unit for Information Science and Artificial Intelligence, University of Hamburg, 1984.

(Hollan *et al.*, 1984) J. Hollan, E. Hutchines, and L. Weitzman. STEAMER: An interactive inspectable simulation-based training system. *AI Magazine*, 5(2):15–28, 1984.

(Hovy *et al.*, 1992) Eduard H. Hovy, Julia L. Lavid, Elisabeth Maier, Vibhu O. Mittal, and Cécile L. Paris. Employing Knowledge Resources in a New Text Planner Architecture. In Robert Dale, Eduard Hovy, Dietmar Rösner, and Oliviero Stock, editors, *Aspects of Automated Natural Language Generation*, pages 57–73. Springer-Verlag, Berlin, 1992.

(Hovy, 1988a) Eduard H. Hovy. *Generating Natural Language Under Pragmatic Constraints*. Lawrence Erlbaum, Hillsdale, New Jersey, 1988.

(Hovy, 1988b) Eduard H. Hovy. Planning Coherent Multisentential Text. In *Proceedings of the Twenty-Sixth Annual Meeting of the Association for Computational Linguistics*, pages 163–169, State University of New York, Buffalo, New York, 7–10 June 1988.

(Jameson and Wahlster, 1982) Antony Jameson and Wolfgang Wahlster. User Modelling in Anaphora Generation: Ellipsis and Definite Description. In *Proceedings of 82 European Conference on Artificial Intelligence (ECAI)*, pages 222–227, 1982.

(Joshi *et al.*, 1984) Aravind Joshi, Bonnie Webber, and Ralph Weischedel. Living Up to Expectations: Computing Expert Responses. In *Proceedings of the Third National Conference on Articifial Intelligence*, pages 169–175, 1984.

(Kaplan, 1982) S. Jerry Kaplan. Cooperative Responses from a Portable Natural Language Query System. *Artificial Intelligence*, 2(19):165–187, 1982.

(Kass, 1991a) Robert Kass. Building a User Model. *User Model and User Adapted Interaction*, 1(3):203–258, 1991.

(Kass, 1991b) Robert Kass. Building a user model implicitly from a cooperative advisory dialog. *User Modeling and User-Adapted Interaction*, 1(3):203–258, 1991.

(Kay, 1979) Martin Kay. Functional Grammar. In *Proceedings of the Fifth Annual Meeting of the Berkeley Linguistic Society*, pages 142–158, 1979.

(Kobsa and Wahlster, 1988) *Computational Linguistics*, Special Issue on User Modeling, September 1988. Volume 14, Number 3.

(Kobsa and Wahlster, 1989) Alfred Kobsa and Wolfgang Wahlster. User Models in Dialog Systems. In Alfred Kobsa and Wolfgang Wahlster, editors, *User Models in Dialog Systems*, pages 4–34. Springer-Verlag, Symbolic Computation Series, Berlin, 1989.

(Kobsa, 1984) Alfred Kobsa. Generating a User Model from WH-Questions in the VIE-LANG System. Technical Report 84–03, Department of Medical Cybernetics, University of Vienna, 1984.

(Kukich, 1983) Karen Kukich. Knowledge-based report generation: A technique for automatically generating natural language reports from databases. In *Proceedings of the Sixth International ACM SIGIR Conference*, Washington, DC, 1983.

(Kukich, 1985) Karen Kukich. Explanation Structures in XSEL. In *Proceedings of the Twenty-Third Annual Meeting of the Association for Computational Linguistics*, University of Chicago, Chicago, Illinois, July 8-12 1985.

(Kwee, 1987) TjoeLiong Kwee. Natural Language Generation. One Individual Implementer's Experience. In *Proceedings of the First European Workshop on Language Generation*, Royaumont, France, January 1987.

(Lancaster and Kolodner, 1987) J. S. Lancaster and J. L. Kolodner. Problem Solving in a Natural Task as a Function of Experience. Technical report, School of Information and Computer Science, Georgia Institute of Technology, Atlanta, Georgia, 1987.

(Lebowitz, 1983a) Michael Lebowitz. Generalization from Natural Language Text. *Cognitive Science*, 7(1):1–40, 1983.

(Lebowitz, 1983b) Michael Lebowitz. RESEARCHER: An Overview. In *Proceedings of the Third National Conference on Artificial Intelligence*, Washington, DC, 1983. American Association of Artificial Intelligence.

(Lebowitz, 1985) Michael Lebowitz. RESEARCHER: An Experimental Intelligent Information System. In *Proceedings of the Ninth International Joint Conference on Artificial Intelligence*, pages 858–862, Los Angeles, 1985.

(Lehnert, 1977) Wendy Lehnert. A Conceptual Theory of Question Answering. In *Proceedings of Fifth International Joint Conference of Artificial Intelligence*, Cambridge, Massachusetts, 1977.

(Lehnert, 1978) Wendy G Lehnert. *The Process of Question Answering*. Lawrence Erlbaum Associates, Hillsdale, New Jersey, 1978.

(Linde and Labov, 1975) C. Linde and W. Labov. Spatial Networks as a Site for the Study of Language and Thought. *Language*, 57–4:924–939, 1975.

(Litman and Allen, 1987) Diane J. Litman and James F. Allen. A Plan Recognition Model for Subdialogues in Conversations. *Cognitive Science*, 11:163–200, 1987.

(McCoy, 1983) Kathleen F. McCoy. Correcting misconceptions: What to say when the user is mistaken. In *Proceedings of the CHI'83; Conference on Human Factors in Computing Systems*, Boston, Ma, 1983.

(McCoy, 1986) Kathleen F. McCoy. The ROMPER System: Responding to Object-Related Misconceptions Using Perspective. In *Proceedings of the Twenty-Fourth Annual Meeting of the Association of Computational Linguistics*, New York City, June 1986.

(McCoy, 1988) Kathleen F. McCoy. Reasoning on a Highlighted User Model to Respond to Misconceptions. *Computational Linguistics*, 14(3):52–63, September 1988.

(McCoy, 1989) Kathleen F. McCoy. Generating Context Sensitive Responses to Object-Related Misconceptions. *Artificial Intelligence*, 41(2):157–195, 1989.

(McDonald, 1980) David D. McDonald. *Natural Language Production as a Process of Decision Making under Constraint*. PhD thesis, MIT, Cambridge, Massasuchetts, 1980.

(McKeown and Elhadad, 1991) Kathleen R. McKeown and Michael Elhadad. Comparison of surface language generators: a case study in choice of connectives. In C. Paris, W. Swartout, and W. Mann, editors, *Natural Language Generation in Artificial Intelligence and Computational Linguistics*. Kluwer Academic Publishers, Boston, 1991.

(McKeown and Paris, 1987) Kathleen R. McKeown and Cécile L. Paris. Functional unification grammar revisited. In *Proceedings of the Twenty-Fifth Annual Meeting of the Association of Computational Linguistics*, Palo Alto, California, 1987.

(McKeown et al., 1985) Kathleen R. McKeown, Myron Wish, and Kevin Matthews. Tailoring Explanations for the User. In *Proceedings of the Ninth International Joint Conference on Artificial Intelligence*, pages 794–798, Los Angeles, California, August 1985.

(McKeown et al., 1992) Kathleen McKeown, Steve Feiner, Jacques Robin, Dorée Seligmann, and Michael Tanenblatt. Generating Cross-References for Multimedia Explanation. In *Proceedings of Tenth National Conference on Artificial Intelligence*, San Jose, California, July 12–17 1992.

(McKeown, 1985) Kathleen R. McKeown. *Text Generation: Using Discourse Strategies and Focus Constraints to Generate Natural Language Text*. Cambridge University Press, Cambridge, England, 1985.

(McKeown, 1988) Kathleen R. McKeown. Generating Goal-Oriented Explanations. *International Journal of Expert Systems*, 1(4):377–395, 1988.

(McTear, 1989) Michael F. McTear. User Modelling and Human-Computer Interaction: A Cognitive Science Perspective. *The Irish Journal of Psychology*, 10:333–352, 1989.

(Mackay and Mountford, 1978) R. Mackay and A. Mountford. *English for Specific Purposes*. Longman, London, 1978.

(Mackinlay, 1986) J. Mackinlay. *Automatic Design of Graphical Presentations*. PhD thesis, Stanford University, Stanford, California, 1986.

(Mann and Thompson, 1987) William C. Mann and Sandra A. Thompson. Rhetorical Structure Theory: A Theory of Text Organization. In Livia Polanyi, editor, *The Structure of Discourse*. Ablex Publishing Corporation, Norwood, New Jersey, 1987.

(Mann and Thompson, 1988) William C. Mann and Sandra A. Thompson. Rhetorical Structure Theory: Towards a Functional Theory of Text Organization. *TEXT*, 8(3):243–281, 1988.

(Mann, 1983) William C. Mann. An Overview of the Penman Text Generation System. In *Proceedings of the Second National Conference on Artificial Intelligence*, pages 261–265, Washington, D.C., 1983.

(Mann, 1984) William C. Mann. Discourse Structures for Text Generation. In *Proceedings of COLING 84*, Stanford, California, July 1984. Association for Computational Linguistics.

(Martin and Rothery, 1981) J. R. Martin and Joan Rothery. The ontogenesis of written genre. *University of Sydney Working Papers in Linguistics*, 2:1–59, 1981.

(Mastaglio, 1990) Thomas Walter Mastaglio. *User Modelling in Cooperative Knowledge-Based Systems*. PhD thesis, Department of Computer Science, University of Colorado, Boulder, 1990.

(Matthiessen and Bateman, 1991) Christian M.I.M. Matthiessen and John A. Bateman. *Text Generation and Systemic Functional Linguistics*. Pinter Publishers, London, 1991.

(Mayfield, 1992) James Mayfield. Controlling inference in plan recognition. *User Modeling and User-Adapted Interaction*, 2(1–2):83–115, 1992.

(Mays, 1980a) Eric Mays. Correcting Misconceptions about Data Base Structure. In *Proceedings 3-CSCSI*, Victoria, B. C., May 1980. Canadian Society of Computational Studies of Intelligence.

(Mays, 1980b) Eric Mays. Failures in Natural Language Systems: Applications to Data Base Query Systems. In *Proceedings of the First National Conference on Artificial Intelligence*, pages 327–330, Stanford, California, August 1980.

(Meteer, 1990) Marie W. Meteer. *The Generation Gap: the problem of expressability in text planning*. PhD thesis, Computer and Information Sciences Department, University of Massachusetts, Amherst, Amherst, Massachusetts, February 1990.

(Mittal and Paris, 1990) Vibhu O. Mittal and Cécile L. Paris. Analogical Explanations. In Kiran Rege and S. Ramani, editors, *Frontiers in Knowledge Based Computing*, pages 17–26. Narosa Publishing House, New Delhi, India, 1990. (Also published as part of the LNCS series by Springer-Verlag).

(Mittal and Paris, 1992) Vibhu O. Mittal and Cécile L. Paris. Generating object descriptions which integrate both text and examples. In *Proceedings of the Ninth*

Canadian Artificial Intelligence Conference (AI/GI/VI 92), pages 1–8. Canadian Society for the Computational Studies of Intelligence (CSCSI), Morgan Kaufmann Publishers, 1992.

(Moore and Paris, 1988) Johanna D. Moore and Cécile L. Paris. Constructing Coherent Text Using Rhetorical Relations. In *Proceedings of the Tenth Annual Conference of the Cognitive Science Society*, pages 637–643, Montreal, Quebec, August 17-19 1988.

(Moore and Paris, 1989) Johanna D. Moore and Cécile L. Paris. Planning Text For Advisory Dialogues. In *Proceedings of the Twenty-Seventh Annual Meeting of the Association for Computational Linguistics*, pages 203–211, Vancouver, B.C., Canada, June 26–29 1989.

(Moore and Paris, 1991) Johanna D. Moore and Cécile L. Paris. Requirements for an Expert System Explanation Facility. *Computational Intelligence*, 7(4), 1991.

(Moore and Paris, 1992a) Johanna D. Moore and Cécile L. Paris. Exploiting user feedback to compensate for the Unreliability of User Models. *User Modeling and User-Adapted Interaction*, 2(4), pages 287–330, 1992.

(Moore and Paris, 1992b) Johanna D. Moore and Cécile L. Paris. Planning Text for Advisory Dialogues: Capturing Intentional, Rhetorical and Attentional Information, 1992. Technical Report from the University of Pittsburgh, Department of Computer Science (Number 92–22) and USC/ISI; Submitted for publication.

(Moore and Swartout, 1989) Johanna D. Moore and William R. Swartout. A Reactive Approach to Explanation. In *Proceedings of the Eleventh International Joint Conference on Artificial Intelligence*, pages 1504–1510, Detroit, Michigan, August 20–25 1989.

(Moore and Swartout, 1991) Johanna D. Moore and William R. Swartout. A Reactive Approach to Explanation: Taking the User's Feedback into Account. In Cécile L. Paris, William R. Swartout, and William C. Mann, editors, *Natural Language Generation in Artificial Intelligence and Computational Linguistics*, pages 3–48. Kluwer Academic Publishers, Boston, 1991.

(Moore, 1989a) Johanna D. Moore. *A Reactive Approach to Explanation in Expert and Advice-Giving Systems*. PhD thesis, University of California, Los Angeles, 1989.

(Moore, 1989b) Johanna D. Moore. Responding to "Huh?": Answering Vaguely Articulated Follow-Up Questions. In *Proceedings of the 1989 Conference on Human Factors in Computing Systems*, pages 91–96, Austin, Texas, April 30–May 4 1989.

(Morik, 1985) Katharina Morik. User modelling, dialog structure, and dialog strategy in HAM-ANS. In *Proceedings of 85 European Association of Computational Linguistics*, Geneva, Switzerland, 1985.

(Morik, 1986) Katharina Morik. Modeling the user's wants. Presented at the First International Workshop on User Modeling, Maria Laach, West Germany, August 1986.

(Neal and Shapiro, 1991) J. Neal and S. Shapiro. Intelligent Multi-Media Interface Technology. In *Intelligent User Interfaces*, pages 11–43. Addison-Wesley, Reading, MA, 1991.

(Neches *et al.*, 1985) Robert Neches, William R. Swartout, and Johanna D. Moore. Enhanced Maintenance and Explanation of Expert Systems Through Explicit Models of Their Development. *IEEE Transactions on Software Engineering*, SE–11(11):1337–1351, November 1985.

(Nessen, 1986) E. Nessen. SCUM; User Modeling in the SINIX-Consultant. In *Presented at the First International Workshop on User Modeling*, Maria Laach, Germany, August 1986.

(New Book of Knowledge, 1967) *The New Book of Knowledge – The Children's Encyclopedia*, 1967. Grolier Inc., New York.

(Nirenburg *et al.*, 1989) Sergei Nirenburg, Eric Nyberg, and Christine Defrise. Text Planning with Opportunistic Control. Technical Report CMU–CM-T-89–113, Center for Machine Translation, Carnegie Mellon University, Pittsburgh, Pennsylvania, 1989.

(O'Donnell, 1990) Michael O'Donnell. A dynamic model of exchange. *Word*, 41(3):293–327, December 1990.

(Paris and Kwee, 1985) Cécile L. Paris and TjoeLiong Kwee. Guide to the unification process and its implementation; progress report on extending the grammar. Technical report, Computer Science Department, Columbia University, New York, New York 10027, 1985.

(Paris and Maier, 1991) Cécile L. Paris and Elisabeth A. Maier. Knowledge Resources or Decisions? In *Proceedings of the IJCAI-91 Workshop on Decision Making throughout the Generation Process*, Sydney, Australia, 1991.

(Paris, 1984) Cécile L. Paris. Determining the Level of Expertise. In *Proceedings of the First Annual Workshop on Theoretical Issues in Conceptual Information Processing*, Atlanta, Georgia, 1984.

(Paris, 1988) Cécile L. Paris. Planning a text: can we and how should we modularize this process?, August 1988. In the *Proceedings of the AAAI–88 Workshop on Text Planning and Realization*.

(Paris, 1991) Cécile L. Paris. Generation and Explanation: Building an Explanation Facility for the Explainable Expert Systems Framework. In Cécile L. Paris, William R. Swartout, and William C. Mann, editors, *Natural Language Generation in Artificial Intelligence and Computational Linguistics*, pages 49–81. Kluwer Academic Publishers, Boston, 1991.

(Patten, 1988) Terry Patten. Compiling the interface between text planning and realization, August 1988. In the *Proceedings of the AAAI–88 Workshop on Text Planning and Realization*.

(Pollack *et al.*, 1982) Martha E. Pollack, Julia Hirschberg, and Bonnie Lynn Webber. User Participation in the Reasoning Processes of Expert Systems. In *Proceedings of the Second National Conference on Artificial Intelligence*, Pittsburgh, Pennsylvania, August 18–20 1982. A longer version of this paper is available as a Technical Report from the University of Pennsylvania, Report Number CIS–82–10.

(Pollack, 1986) Martha E. Pollack. A Model of Plan Inference that Distinguishes Between the Beliefs of Actors and Observers. In *Proceedings of the Twenty-Fourth Annual Meeting of the Association for Computational Linguistics*, pages 207–214, New York, June 1986.

(Quilici *et al.*, 1988) Alex Quilici, Dyer Michael, and Flowers Margot. Providing Explanatory Responses to Plan-Oriented Misconceptions. *Computational Linguistics*, 14(3):38–51, September 1988.

(Quilici, 1989) Alex Quilici. Detecting and responding to plan-oriented misconceptions. In Alfred Kobsa and Wolfgang Wahlster, editors, *User Models in Dialog Systems*. Springer Verlag, Symbolic Computation Series, Berlin, 1989.

(Raskutti and Zukerman, 1991) Bhavani Raskutti and Ingrid Zukerman. Generation and selection of likely interpretation during plan recognition in task-oriented consultation systems. *User Modeling and User-Adapted Interaction*, 1(4):323–353, 1991.

(Reader's Digest, 1989) Reader's Digest,, September 1989. Contributed by Arlene Shovald.

(Reichlis and Lemon, 1952) Reichlis and Lemon. *Exploring Physics*. Harcourt, Brace and Company. Inc., 1952.

(Retz-Schmidt, 1991) Gudula Retz-Schmidt. Recognizing intentions, interactions, and causes of plan failures. *User Modeling and User-Adapted Interaction*, 1(2):173–202, 1991.

(Rich, 1979) Elaine Rich. User Modeling via Stereotypes. *Cognitive Science*, 3:329–354, 1979.

(Roth *et al.*, 1991) S. Roth, J. Mattis, and X. Mesnard. Graphics and Natural Language as Components of Automatic Explanation. In *Intelligent User Interfaces*, pages 207–239. Addison-Wesley, Reading, Massachusetts, 1991.

(Rubinoff, 1992) Robert Rubinoff. Integrating text planning and linguistic choice by annotating linguistic structures. In Robert Dale, Eduard Hovy, Dietmar Rösner, and Oliviero Stock, editors, *Aspects of Automated Natural Language Generation*, pages 45–56. Springer-Verlag, Berlin, 1992.

(Sarner and Carberry, 1992) Margaret Sarner and Sandra Carberry. Generating tailored definitions using a multifaceted user model. *User Modeling and User-Adapted Interaction*, 2(3):181–210, 1992.

(Schank and Abelson, 1977) R. C. Schank and R. P. Abelson. *Scripts, Plans, Goals and Understanding*. Lawrence Erlbaum Associates, Hillsdale, New Jersey, 1977.

(Shepherd, 1926) H. R. Shepherd. *The Fine Art of Writing*. The Macmillan Co, New York, 1926.

(Shifroni and Shanon, 1992) Eyal Shifroni and Benny Shanon. Interactive user modeling: An integrative explicit-implicit approach. *User Modeling and User-Adapted Interaction*, 2, 1992.

(Sibun, 1992) Penelope Sibun. Generating Text without Trees. *Computational Intelligence*, 8(1), 1992.

(Sidner and Israel, 1981) Candace L. Sidner and David Israel. Recognizing Intended Meaning and Speaker's Plans. In *Proceedings of the Seventh International Joint Conference on Artificial Intelligence*, pages 203–208, Vancouver, B. C., Canada, August 1981.

(Sidner, 1979) Candace L. Sidner. *Toward a Computational Theory of Definite Anaphora Comprehension in English Discourse*. PhD thesis, Massachusetts Institute of Technology, Cambridge, Massachusetts., 1979.

(Sidner, 1985) Candace L. Sidner. Plan Parsing for Intended Response Recognition in Discourse. *Computational Intelligence*, 1(1):1–10, 1985.

(Simon and Schuster, 1972) *The Way Things Work*. Simon and Schuster, New York, 1972.

(Sleeman and Brown, 1981) Derek H. Sleeman and John Seely Brown, editors. *Intelligent Tutoring Systems*. Academic Press, London, 1981.

(Sleeman, 1982) Derek H. Sleeman. Inferring Mal Rules From Pupil's Protocols. In *Proceedings of the 6th European Conference on Artificial Intelligence*, pages 160–164, Orsay, France, 1982.

(Sleeman, 1983) Derek H. Sleeman. Inferring Student Models for Intelligent Computer-Aided Instruction. In R. S. Michalski and J. G. Carbonell annd T. M. Mitchell, editors, *Machine Learning: An Artificial Intelligence Appproach*. Tioga, 1983.

(Sleeman, 1985) Derek H. Sleeman. UMFE: A User Modelling Front End SubSystem. *International Journal of Man-Machine Studies*, 23:71–88, 1985.

(Stedman, 1982) *Stedman's Medical Dictionary*, Baltimore, London, Los Angeles, Sydney, 1982. Williams and Wilkins. 24th Edition.

(Stevens and Steinberg, 1981) Albert Stevens and Cindy Steinberg. A Typology of Explanations and its Application to Intelligent Computer Aided Instruction. Technical Report 4626, Bolt Beranek and Newman, Inc, Boston, Massachusetts, 1981.

(Stevens et al., 1979) A. Stevens, A. Collins, and S. E. Goldin. Misconceptions in Student's Understanding. *International Journal of Man-Machine Studies*, 11:145–156, 1979.

(Suthers, 1991) Daniel D. Suthers. Task-appropriate hybrid architectures for explanation. *Computational Intelligence*, 7(4), 1991.

(Swartout and Smoliar, 1987) William R. Swartout and Stephen W. Smoliar. On Making Expert Systems More Like Experts. *Expert Systems*, 4(3):196–207, August 1987.

(Swartout et al., 1991) William R. Swartout, Cécile L. Paris, and Johanna D. Moore. Design for Explainable Expert Systems. *IEEE Expert*, 6(3):58–64, June 1991.

(Tennant, 1978) Harry Tennant. The Evaluation of Natural Language Question Answerers. Technical report, University of Illinois at Urbana/Champaign, 1978. Ph.D. Proposal, Department of Computer Science, Advanced Automation Group, Coordinated Science Laboratory.

(Tennant, 1981) Harry Tennant. *Natural Language Processing*. Petrocelli Books, Inc., 1981.

(Ure and Ellis, 1969) Jean Ure and J. Ellis. Language varieties – register. In Meetham et al., editor, *Encyclopedia of Linguistics (Information and Control)*, volume 12, pages 251–259. Pergammon Press, Oxford, 1969.

(Ure, 1969) Jean Ure. Practical registers. *English Language Teaching Journal*, 23(2 and 3), 1969.

(van Beek, 1986) Peter van Beek. A Model for User Specific Explanations from Expert Systems. Technical Report CS-86-42, University of Waterloo, Canada, 1986.

(van Beek, 1987) Peter van Beek. A model for generating better explanations. In *Proceedings of the Twenty-Fifth Annual Meeting of the Association of Computational Linguistics*, Palo Alto, California, 1987.

(van Dijk, 1980) T.A. van Dijk. *Macrostructures. An interdisciplinary study of global structures in discourse, interaction and cognition*. Mouton, The Hague, 1980.

(van Hahn et al., 1980) W. van Hahn, W. Hoeppner, A. Jamewon, and W. Walster. The Anatomy of the Natural Language Dialogue System HAM-RPM. In L. Bolc, editor, *Natural Language based Computer Systems*. Hanser/Macmillan, Munich, 1980.

(Ventola, 1983) Eija Ventola. Contrasting Schematic Structures in Service Encounters. *Applied Linguistics*, 4, 1983.

(Ventola, 1984) Eija Ventola. The dynamics of genre. *Nottingham Linguistics Circular*, 14, 1984.

(Verwiebe *et al.*, 1962) F.L. Verwiebe, G. R. Van Hooft, and Suchy R. R. *Physics; A Basic Science*. D. van Nostrand Company, Inc., Princeton, New Jersey, 1962.

(Wahlster and Kobsa, 1989) Wolfgang Wahlster and Alfred Kobsa. User Models in Dialog Systems. In Alfred Kobsa and Wolfgang Wahlster, editors, *User Models in Dialog Systems*, pages 4–34. Springer Verlag, Symbolic Computation Series, Berlin, 1989.

(Wahlster *et al.*, 1978) W. Wahlster, A. Jameson, and W. Hoeppner. Glancing, Referring, and Explaining in the Dialogue System HAM-RPM. *American Journal of Computational Linguistics*, pages 53–67, 1978.

(Wahlster *et al.*, 1990) Wolfgang Wahlster, Elisabeth André, S. Bandyopadhyay, Winfried Graf, and Thomas Rist. WIP: The Coordinated Generation of Multimodal Presentations from a Common Representation. In *Proc. Int. Workshop on Computational Theories of Communication and their Applications: Problems and Prospects*, Trentino, Italy, November 1990.

(Wahlster *et al.*, 1991) Wolfgang Wahlster, Elisabeth André, Winfried Graf, and Thomas Rist. Designing Illustrated Texts: How Language Production is Influenced by Graphics Generation. In *Proc. European Chapter of the Assoc. for Computational Linguistics*, pages 8–14, Berlin, April 1991.

(Wallis and Shortliffe, 1982) J. W. Wallis and E. H. Shortliffe. Explanatory power for medical expert systems: Studies in the representation of causal relationships for clinical consultations. *Methods of Information in Medicine*, 21:127–136, 1982.

(Wasserman and Lebowitz, 1983) Kenneth Wasserman and Michael Lebowitz. Representing complex physical objects. *Cognition and Brain Theory*, 6(3):333–352, 1983.

(Wasserman, 1985) Kenneth Wasserman. *Unifying Representation and Generalization: Understanding Hierarchically Structured Objects*. PhD thesis, Columbia University Department of Computer Science, New York, 1985.

(Webster, 1979) *Webster's New Twentieth Century Dictionary*, New York, 1979. New World Dictionaries. Second Edition.

(Weiner, 1980) J. Weiner. BLAH, a System that Explains its Reasoning. *Artificial Intelligence Journal*, 15:19–48, 1980.

(Weissler and Weissler, 1973) A. Weissler and P. Weissler. *A Woman's Guide to Fixing the Car*. Walker and Company, New York, 1973.

(Wenger, 1987) Etienne Wenger. *Artificial Intelligence and Tutoring Systems: Computational and Cognitive Approaches to the Communication of Knowledge*. Morgan Kaufmann Publishers, Los Altos, California, 1987.

(White, 1974) R. White. Communicative competence, registers, and second language. *International Review of Applied Linguistics*, 12(2):127–141, 1974.

(Wilensky *et al.*, 1984) Robert Wilensky, Yigal Arens, and David Chin. Talking to UNIX in English: An Overview of UC. *Communications of the Association for Computing Machinery*, 27(6):575–593, 1984.

(Williams, 1893) W. Williams. *Composition and Rhetoric*. D.C. Heath and Co., Boston, Mass, 1893.

(Wilson and Anderson, 1986) P. T. Wilson and R. C. Anderson. What They Don't Know Will Hurt Them: The Role of Prior Knowledge in Comprehension. In Orasanu, editor, *Reading Comprehension: From Research to Practice*. Erlbaum, Hillsdale, New Jersey, 1986.

(Winograd and Flores, 1986) T. Winograd and F. Flores. *Understanding computers and cognition*. Ablex Publishing Company, Norwood, New Jersey, 1986.

(Wolz *et al.*, 1990) Ursula Wolz, Kathleen R. McKeown, and Gail E. Kaiser. Automated Tutoring in Interactive Environments: A Task-Centered Approach. *Machine-Mediated Learning*, 3(1):53–79, 1990.

(Wolz, 1990) Ursula Wolz. The impact of user modeling on text generation in task-oriented settings. In *Proceedings of the Second International Workshop on User Modeling*. AAAI and the University of Hawaii, 1990.

(Woods, 1973) W. Woods. An Experimental Parsing System for Transition Network Grammars. In R. Rustin, editor, *Natural Language Processing*. Algorithmics Press, New York, 1973.

(Wu, 1991) Dekai Wu. Active Acquisition of User Models: Implications for Decision-Theoretic Dialog Planning and Plan Recognition. *Journal of User Model and User Adapted Interaction*, 1(2):149–172, 1991.

Index